FINANCIAL TIMES
MANAGEMENT

Knowledge   Skills   Understanding

Financial Times Management is a new business created
to deliver the knowledge, skills and understanding that
will enable students, managers and organisations to
achieve their ambitions, whatever their needs,
wherever they are.

To find out more about Financial Times Management
visit our website at:

www.ftmanagement.com

Financial Times Management Briefings are happy to receive proposals from individuals who have expertise in the field of management education.

If you would like to discuss your ideas further, please contact Andrew Mould, Commissioning Editor.

Tel: 0171 447 2210
Fax: 0171 240 5771
e-mail: andrew.mould@ftmanagement.com

Decision Support Using Data Mining

SARABJOT S. ANAND

ALEX G. BÜCHNER

Information Technology

FINANCIAL TIMES
MANAGEMENT

LONDON · HONG KONG · JOHANNESBURG
MELBOURNE · SINGAPORE · WASHINGTON DC

FINANCIAL TIMES MANAGEMENT
128 Long Acre, London WC2E 9AN
Tel: +44 (0)171 447 2000
Fax: +44 (0)171 240 5771
Website: www.ftmanagement.com

A Division of Financial Times Professional Limited

First published in Great Britain in 1998

ISBN 0 273 63269 8

British Library Cataloguing in Publication Data
A CIP catalogue record for this book can be obtained from the British Library.

10 9 8 7 6 5 4 3 2 1

Printed and bound in Great Britain.

The Publishers' policy is to use paper manufactured from sustainable forests.

About the authors

Sarabjot S. Anand is presently employed as a Research Fellow in Advanced Knowledge-based Systems, at the Northern Ireland Knowledge Engineering Laboratory, University of Ulster, Northern Ireland.

Mr Anand joined the School of Information and Software Engineering at the University of Ulster in 1992. In January 1996 he was appointed to his present position in the Northern Ireland Knowledge Engineering Laboratory. Mr Anand is presently responsible for the transfer of data mining technology to industry. He has been involved in a number of successfully completed projects in data mining and is presently working on technology transfer projects in the financial, manufacturing, medical and software sectors. One of his major interests in the area of technology transfer is in the setting up of collaborative projects outside the UK.

Mr Anand has research interests in database technology, knowledge-based systems, machine learning, parallel algorithms and data mining. He has been working in the field of data mining since 1993 and has published over 20 papers in these areas.

In 1994 he established the University of Ulster Data Mining Interest Group that focuses on data mining research carried out in the Faculty of Informatics. The Group has over 40 members at present from industrial and academic institutions in Northern Ireland and the Republic of Ireland.

Alex G. Büchner is also employed by the Northern Ireland Knowledge Engineering Laboratory at the University of Ulster. In his current position as Research Fellow he is working in the area of data mining and is involved in several related projects in Europe and the Far East.

After completing his degree in Information Technology and Business Studies in Germany, and having various positions developing database and client-server applications, he obtained an MSc in Software Engineering from the University of Abertay, Dundee, Scotland, and went on to lecture in the same institution. He is currently a candidate for the doctoral degree.

Mr Büchner's main research interests are in the fields of knowledge discovery, object-oriented technologies, multi-databases, electronic commerce and internationalisation. He has written more than ten publications in these fields.

CONTENTS

PREFACE

This book is aimed at organisations that intend to remain competitive in their sector, as data mining is an essential ingredient for strategic decision support.

Decision support systems that provide organisations with accurate information in a timely fashion are a requirement in today's competitive world where information technology (IT) is not just a frill but a requirement. The focus of investments in IT has changed from business process automation tools to operational strategy tools. Data mining provides the required tools for drilling into the large databases containing production data and discovering useful information that can help in decision support.

The book provides information on how to go about navigating this change in the IT landscape, moving from on-line transaction processing (OLTP) systems to data warehousing, multi-dimensional databases, on-line analytical processing (OLAP) and, of course, data mining. It differentiates between data mining and related areas associated with data mining, describes the various stages of the process of data mining, the common mistakes made when implementing a data mining solution in the real-world and the business process reengineering required to gear the organisation for data mining. It also describes case studies in data mining and provides guidance on how to select the tool that is right for the data mining task at hand.

The report has three main audiences. First, it provides the management of an organisation with the idea of what data mining can do for them, by explaining what data mining is and how it fits into the complex IT landscape. Second, it provides guidelines to IT managers in data mining client organisations by explaining the required stages of a pilot or full-scale data mining project, thereby illustrating how such a project should be managed and how much effort is required by the IT department. Third, it provides guidelines for data mining service providers as to a standard practice that they should employ to ensure successful implementation of their projects.

To get the most out of this book, we suggest that it be approached by the different audiences in different ways, as described below.

- Decision makers should read the whole report to arm themselves with the required knowledge of data mining to realise its benefits to their organisation. At this stage Chapters 4 and 5 may be skimmed over as their objective is to provide advice during a data mining project.

- Clients involved in data mining projects should also read the whole report but in addition they should treat Chapter 4 as a benchmark on how to go about a data mining project. Chapter 5 may be used as a reference during the problem specification and methodology identification stages of the project.

- Data mining service providers, should use Chapter 4 as a guideline to a standard practice that they should employ to ensure successful implementation of their projects.

ACKNOWLEDGEMENTS

We would like to acknowledge the help and guidance that we have received during the preparation of this book, as well as during the various data mining projects that we have worked on which have led to many of the ideas that are presented here. In particular, we would like to thank Professor David Bell, School of Information and Software Engineering, University of Ulster, and Professor John Hughes, Director of Northern Ireland Knowledge Engineering Laboratory and Dean of the Faculty of Informatics, University of Ulster, for their encouragement throughout the years. We would also like to acknowledge Maurice Mulvenna for his valuable expertise in business process reengineering. We also appreciate all the members of the Data Mining Interest Group* who provided a wonderfully uninhibited environment in which to bounce off new ideas in the field.

Thanks must also go to all the staff of the Northern Ireland Knowledge Engineering Laboratory for providing us with the time and facilities to carry out our research and writing of this book, especially David Patterson and Alan Patrick for proofreading the document and providing useful suggestions and improvements.

The work that led to the formation of a lot of the ideas presented in this book was funded by the Industrial Research and Technology Unit, Northern Ireland, under various funding programmes. We would like to acknowledge and thank them for their support.

We are also grateful to all our industrial partners for their support and for providing us with challenging real-world problems and data sets.

---

*   http://iserve1.infj.ulst.ac.uk:8080/

We are also delighted that James Mace from British Telecom plc, Mark Beamont from Angoss Software Ltd and Colin Shearer from Integral Solutions Ltd. were willing to provide us with industrial case studies.

Finally, we would like to thank our friends and relations for all their patience and for bearing up with all the 'mood swings' that we went through during the preparation of this book.

MANAGEMENT SUMMARY

To gain the most profitable output from data mining for a decision-making process, a state-of-the-art enterprise has to be aware of four major key factors:

1. Why is data mining needed?

2. How does data mining work?

3. What strategic changes are required?

4. Where can data mining expertise be obtained?

The need for data mining has arisen from a change in the perceived use of IT in the industry from a process automator to an information provider. The recent explosion of amounts of data and the subsequent scenario of not being able to track hidden information from it has generated an interest in software tools that can sift through data and discover what information is embedded in it that could be potentially useful to the decision maker in the organisation. This shift in the role of IT within organisations to an 'info-centric' resource has brought to light a number of weaknesses in the IT infrastructure typically found in organisations, one such example being the masses of data distributed in heterogeneous and inconsistent legacy systems. Also, data formats are geared more towards on-line transaction processing that have very different needs from decision support applications. These examples highlight the need for data warehousing.

Data warehousing integrates data from distributed legacy systems, enhancing it using externally procured data and aligning it with the business needs of the organisation. Another aspect of data warehousing is making decision support information available to decision makers in the organisations. Advanced database reporting tools, query languages, statistical packages, machine learning tools and on-line analytical processing are some of the tools available to the decision maker to extract useful information from data warehouses. However, they do not cover a number of decision support requirements and only allow manually guided discovery of useful information, ruling out discovery of truly unexpected information. Data mining, on the other hand, attempts to discover information that the decision maker has little insight of.

As in any other engineering discipline, data mining can be divided into a series of steps arranged as a process. To employ this data mining process successfully, 12 steps have been identified that should be followed to ensure the success of a data mining project:

Step 1: Identify a motivated data and domain expert.

Step 2: Identify the data mining tasks in the problem and map them onto their data mining goals.

Step 3: Identify the user of the output of the data mining tasks and the required knowledge representation scheme.

Step 4: Identify the relevant data for each data mining task and determine its accessibility and usefulness: *Let the data speak for itself as opposed to using any user bias that is not fully justified.*

Step 5: Identify attribute generalisations, attribute dependencies, environmental constraints and any knowledge about the domain known to domain experts.

Step 6: Take the domain, format of input data, acquired domain knowledge and output requirements into account when deciding on the methodology to be used.

Step 7: Pre-process the data by filling in missing values, by enriching it through buying any useful external data available, by identifying and removing outliers, by resolving heterogeneity, and by coding the data, as well as by reducing its dimensionality and size.

Step 8: Choose algorithm parameters carefully and discover regularities/patterns in the data.

Step 9: Filter out uninteresting and obvious patterns.

Step 10: Validate the interesting patterns.

Step 11: Set up a knowledge maintenance mechanism.

Step 12: Ask the question: 'Are we actually better off now than we were before we started the data mining exercise?'

To facilitate data mining properly within an enterprise, strategic modifications have to be accepted, which include not only human resource changes and enhancements of the technological infrastructure, but also business process reorganisation. Human resources involved in the data mining process embody domain expertise which, based on the problem at hand, may vary. Data expertise is usually provided by a database administrator, and data mining expertise is concerned with all steps of the data mining process. Due to the fact that data accessibility and knowledge handling are crucial in a data mining environment, the information technology landscape would be best suited within a data warehouse which provides those facilities. To tackle inevitable performance bottlenecks, parallelised software and hardware support is a very supportive technology.

The synergy between business process reengineering (BPR) and data mining leads to an environment in which ideal knowledge discovery can be promised. The amalgamation of the two disciplines can be employed on the first-order (or morphostatic) level, i.e. the transition from traditional OLTP to OLAP and data warehousing, as well as on the second-order (or morphogenic) level, i.e. the full integration of data mining in a data warehouse, which acts as the major component of a decision-making process. In addition to general BPR requirements, which are expressed as commonly utilised success factors, also branch-specific needs have to be considered to allow data mining to be successfully embodied in a modern enterprise.

Data mining is not an off-the-shelf tool; it is a sophisticated technology which has to be supported by a battery of facilities and, optionally, by an external service provider. Evaluating available products should be orientated as close to the data mining process as possible and criteria for their evaluation have to be chosen carefully, because there is no omnipotent data mining software – and there never will be. But, with an appropriately chosen data mining landscape, knowledge discovered from data will provide indispensable information for prosperous decision making.

1

Introduction

Information Technology (IT) has in the last two decades revolutionised businesses ranging from small enterprises to large multinational companies. Today, the Internet and multimedia are household words. Seldom has a technology had such a profound effect on our lives.

The effect of the IT revolution has had an even greater impact on industry in the last 25 years. Initial IT investments in industry were aimed at the automation of business processes. This led to the generation of large amounts of data that was stored for the purpose of producing reports and summary information indicating to higher management how the companies were performing.

However, the business environment has evolved and in the present competitive conditions just producing historical reports or performing retrospective analyses of the effect of managerial decisions on the organisation's performance is insufficient. Today, for a company to progress, it must respond rapidly to the customer's needs and strive towards better developments in competitive organisation marketing strategies. Organisations now find that they require an effective strategy to retain their present customers let alone woo new ones. For example, organisations from airlines to retailers are bringing in new and novel loyalty schemes. Organisations that were not planning on such schemes now find that they are left with no choice if they are to remain competitive. However, such loyalty schemes, if introduced without proper planning or on an uninformed basis can cost an organisation more than they are worth. This is the reason why organisational investments in IT are now moving from 'automating to informating' (Butler Group, 1996). Today, information has become one of the most important assets of a business.

Nevertheless, most organisations find that their IT infrastructure is unable to support such 'info-searching' activities. This is mainly due to the fact that initial IT investments were aimed at on-line transaction processing (OLTP) rather than decision support purposes. For example, the initial goal of banks was to automate customer transactions which were carried out at an account level. Thus, one customer with five accounts within the bank represented five different entities to the bank. Such a situation, while acceptable from the viewpoint of transaction processing, is clearly unacceptable for decision support purposes. Also, as the nature of OLTP applications is completely different from those required for decision support, present IT infrastructure, optimised for OLTP, is very inefficient for decision support activities.

1.1   DECISION SUPPORT SYSTEMS

> Where is the wisdom we have lost in knowledge? Where is the knowledge we have lost in information?

T. S. Eliot

In today's info-centric, competitive environment, the need for decisions made using timely and accurate knowledge is more apparent than ever before. However, rather than hearing about robust tools for accessing the much required knowledge, we are more used to hearing about the information overload. Thus, the quote by Eliot above is very relevant to the situation that top executives and decision makers find themselves in. It is the role of a good decision support system to be able to discern real knowledge from information and make that knowledge available for the decision maker, who can then use his/her wisdom to arrive at a decision. It is this wisdom that cannot be dispensed with and which makes a decision maker central to the effectiveness of the decision support system, thus differentiating it from a decision-making system.

Decision making may be considered as consisting of three phases (Scott Morton, 1960): *intelligence, design and choice*. Intelligence is the phase of locating a problem within the business environment that requires a decision to be made. Design is the formulation of possible alternative solutions to the problem, while choice involves the selection of the 'optimal' solution. The definition of optimality is based on the objective associated with the decision to be made. For example, if the decision to be made is to pick a route to be taken from point A to point B, each alternative route may be optimal in its own right – one may be the shortest, another the least congested and so on. Therefore, it is only when a specific objective is used that one alternative can be judged as better than the other, i.e. if the objective is to cover the minimum mileage, the first path from A to B would be optimal. Note that, based on how thorough the design stage of decision making was, the optimal solution arrived at during the choice stage may in fact be globally suboptimal. A structured decision problem is one in which all these three phases may potentially be automated. These are situations where the problem is well formulated as are the constraints on the possible solutions. The optimal solution is chosen based on a well-formulated decision function using mathematical or stochastic techniques like Operations Research. Gorry and Scott Morton (1991), in what is considered the foundation paper on decision support systems, suggest that computerised solutions to such problems are decision-making systems rather than decision support systems as they can function independently of human intervention.

On the other hand a semi-structured problem is one where one or more phases of decision making are not possible to automate. Such problems normally require expert advise in formulating an optimal or 'best' solution, which is normally arrived at using rules of thumb and heuristics gained through experience. Knowledge-based systems (KBS) or expert systems have had a profound effect on providing computerised support for decision making in such problem environments. Initial solutions used rule-based expert systems that required the elicitation of knowledge from domain experts and its modelling and coupling with an effective inference engine to utilise the knowledge in different decision-making situations. However, such solutions met with mixed success mainly due to the bottleneck process of knowledge elicitation from the domain expert.

A newer paradigm for implementing KBS, namely case-based reasoning (CBR), provided a solution to this bottleneck by removing the requirement for knowledge elicitation and structuring. CBR models the way humans approach problem solving, i.e. to solve a problem, *remember* a similar problem you have solved earlier and *adapt* the old solution to solve the new problem. CBR systems consist of a case base and a set of adaptation rules. When presented with a new problem, the most similar cases are retrieved from the case base and their solutions are adapted using the adaptation rules as best as possible. Note that this is very similar to the decision-making phases — intelligence, design and choice — where the design and choice phases are implemented using the CBR system. However, most real-world implementations of CBR systems are more case-based retrieval systems as opposed to case-based reasoning systems. The main reason for this is that adaptation knowledge needs to be elicited from domain experts which brings us back to the original bottleneck faced in the development of rule-based systems.

So why do we need KBS in decision making when humans are so adept at making decisions? First, real experts are few and far between – the reason being that most complex processes require copious amounts of knowledge for decision making. Such knowledge can only be assimilated through experience – not through theoretical learning. One statistic states that it takes ten years of knowledge assimilation by a genius before he or she can produce a truly remarkable piece of work! In such environments, KBS can go a long way in assisting in the decision process.

KBS have also proved their worth in scheduling problems that are not as well defined as required by decision-making systems. Scheduling involves assigning times and resources to activities so that a set of constraints is best satisfied according to a set of predefined objectives. It is a difficult problem and much of the difficulty comes from the need to schedule a large number of activities, and to attend to a diverse set of objectives, requirements and constraints which are often in conflict with each other. A good schedule must reflect a satisfactory compromise among these competing influences. Often these requirements are hard to formalise into the format required by decision-making systems. Because of the amount of information involved and the complexity of the scheduling process, human schedulers typically do not handle them well. They usually employ simple rules and consider limited information to approach a (or any) solution which is often of merely short-term benefit. Knowledge-based scheduling systems (KBSS) are employed to find the optimal solution. The data and information used by the KBSS are provided by both the company's management information systems (MIS) and the human schedulers. Human knowledge and judgement is thus built into the KBSS and knowledge-based algorithms are then used during the decision-making process. The KBSS itself could not make the decisions intelligently unless it is armed with the relevant knowledge (the strategies and the rules of thumb) from the decision makers. The more information about the jobs and the shop floor the KBSS obtains from the MIS and the planner, the more correct and faultless schedules the KBSS constructs.

Thus, knowledge-based solutions to hard problems are now commonplace in industry based on different KBS paradigms. However, these systems still rely on the availability of concise and high-quality knowledge on the part of the experts within the organisation and its correct interpretation and representation by the knowledge engineer. Also, due to the continuous evolving of business processes, the usefulness of static knowledge may be questioned in dynamic domains.

Managerial activity may be classified into three categories: operational control, management control and strategic planning (Anthony, 1965). Gorry and Scott Morton (1971) described the class of unstructured strategic planning tasks as the area that requires maximum effort in providing decision support as this is the area of maximum payoffs. Decision support systems were to be an accessory to decision makers that would help them improve their decision process and extend their capabilities, not replace them. An important role of these systems would be to make available high-quality information. Information required for strategic planning is available within on-line transaction processing databases that are modelling various aspects of the company's business. OLTP databases, a result of initial IT investment as operation/process automators, are generally available in organisations today. However, technologies for handling these floods of data and sifting through them to provide appropriate information in a concise form were not available, frustrating decision makers. Thus, there was a clear need felt for new technologies for use in strategic planning. The situation is summed up in Fig. 1.1.

Figure 1.1
THE TECHNOLOGY GAP AND THE IT RESPONSE

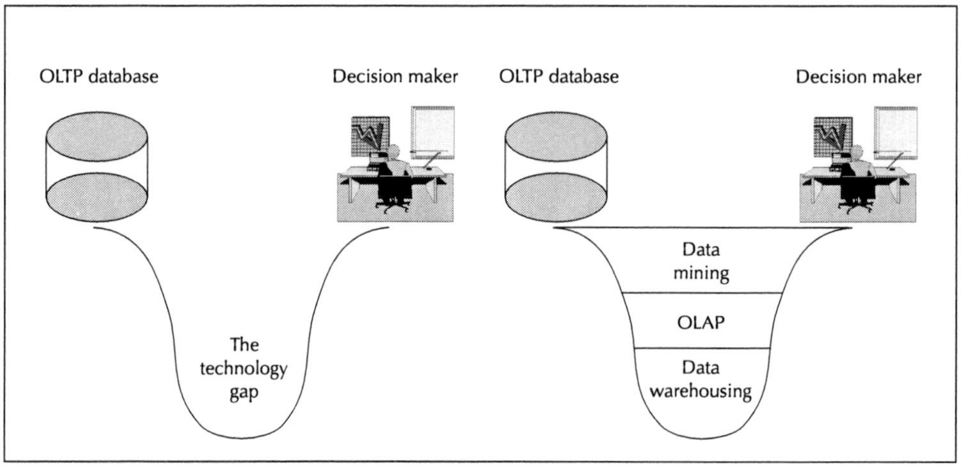

1.2   THE DEMAND FOR THE NEW TECHNOLOGY

So the needs of the industry are changing and the expectations from IT have moved towards information provision rather than process automation. With this change in expectation it is only natural that IT providers must respond with new technologies aimed at providing solutions to the industry's needs. Data warehouses, on-line analytical processing (OLAP) and now data mining are just some of the new technologies that have emerged in the last decade for this purpose.

One resource that seems to have been ignored by most of these previous attempts at providing information for decision support has been the large data sources that have been accumulated in operational OLTP systems. This data contains information on the business performance and trends imbedded in it that, if harnessed, could greatly enhance the decision-making capability of the organisation.

Figure 1.2
THE CENTRALISED ARCHITECTURE OF DATA MANAGEMENT

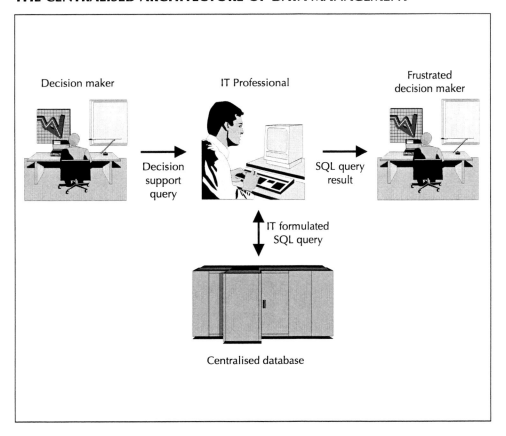

One major contributing factor in this low utilisation of the data resource has been historical. Database systems were initially implemented as centralised data stores with access restricted to the IT department (see Fig.1.2). As a result, data was not within easy access of the decision makers. Whenever the decision makers required any information from the database, they had to put in a request to the IT department who formulated the required query. The database management system produced reams of paper as the query result that often did not match the decision maker's original requirement. The reason for this mismatch is very similar to the problem faced in knowledge acquisition by the domain experts and knowledge engineers and is a direct result of both being novices in the other person's field. Another reason is the fact that the nature of decision making makes it difficult to formulate the exact requirements immediately, and it is through iterative refinement of the queries that final requirements are formulated. Also, the queries required to provide the decision makers with their reports were complex when compared to the OLTP queries for which the database systems were designed. Thus, they were run in batch mode when the OLTP load was not high. So the resources available for such queries were limited and repeated requests for refinements often led to friction between IT professionals and the decision makers.

Slowly, the database systems changed to a distributed architecture as opposed to centralised (*see* Fig. 1.3). The new environment placed the data in the hands of the decision makers in each department within the organisation, who were now entrusted with the data pertaining to their business. The departments found their own IT gurus and slowly the departmental database systems drifted away from each other and inconsistencies started to develop between the different database systems. The realisation on the part of the decision makers that decisions at departmental levels also require a global view of the organisation and therefore access to data from other departments, led to dissatisfaction with this architecture as well. Now, along with the frustration of the decision makers due to unavailability of data, there was the added frustration for the IT professionals due to the incompatibility and inconsistency of the distributed data.

Figure 1.3
THE DISTRIBUTED ARCHITECTURE OF DATA MANAGEMENT

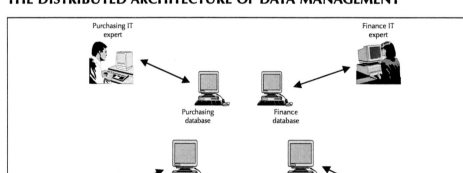

The inadequacies of SQL and database reporting tools for use in decision support were also becoming obvious and the inability of client software like spreadsheets and statistical packages to fill this gap was also becoming apparent. Thus, the industry was crying out for new technology that addressed their decision support needs. Data warehousing, OLAP and data mining aim to exploit this largely untapped resource.

Figure 1.4
THE INFORMATION SUPPLY CHAIN

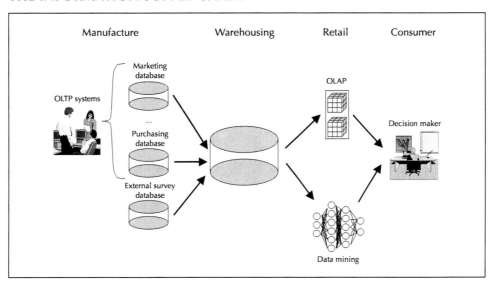

An analogy is drawn with the manufacturing sector by Kenan Systems Corporation (Kenan Sahin, 1996) to explain how OLTP systems, data warehouses and OLAP systems fit into the decision support IT landscape. Just as manufacturing industries divide their business into the three stages of production, warehousing and retailing, the supply of data to the user, who is normally a manager or executive, must follow the same three stages (*see* Fig. 1.4). OLTP systems are on the production end of the spectrum as it is where the data used for decision support is generated. The large amount of data produced by the OLTP system remains inaccessible to the user, just as the retailers do not get access to the production units of the manufacturer. OLTP data needs to be repackaged before the user can use it. This is mainly due to the shortcomings of the OLTP systems outlined in section 2.2. Data collected in OLTP systems is enhanced, cleansed and consolidated before being stored in a data warehouse that provides an environment that parallels the users' understanding of their business. OLAP systems are the retailers. Data is stored in a user-oriented fashion in multi-dimensional databases (*see* section 2.3.3), sometimes referred to as the OLAP server, and tools for accessing and analysing this data are provided to the user. The OLAP server may be used as a front-end to the OLTP server itself; however, it is usually used in conjunction with a data warehouse. The multi-dimensional database contains aggregations of the underlying warehouse or OLTP data along dimensions defined by the user. Automated drill-down facilities that allow the user to view the detailed data are usually provided by the multi-dimensional database, which is one of the reasons that a warehouse is recommended to relieve the OLTP systems from the extra load. Rather than user-led packaging and retailing provided by OLAP, the user directing the search for information, data mining is an alternative retailer of knowledge which incorporates additional elements of automation. The user now needs to provide only a loose/vague description of the objective of the decision to be made and the data mining software will sift through the relevant data and discover useful knowledge.

1.3 DATA MINING: LOOKING BEYOND THE TIP OF THE ICEBERG

Data mining has been defined as the 'tireless and relentless searching of data for useful patterns' (*Byte*, 1995). This tireless and relentless searching can either be automatic or manually guided. Manually guided systems have the disadvantage that the type of patterns searched for need to be conceived by the user and less obvious patterns remain undiscovered. Query and reporting tools, as well as OLAP, fall into the category of manually guided systems, whereas data mining tools are automated discovery tools which allow for user biases (i.e. are semi-automated). While data mining systems to date cannot realistically deal with queries of the type 'Give me something interesting that could be useful', the goal of data mining would be to provide support for such queries.

Data mining is the name given to automated searching systems that still require a certain amount of input from the user but which do not need to be directed by the user as to what patterns have to be discovered – this is sometimes referred to as 'semi-automisation'. Pseudonyms of data mining in common use are knowledge discovery in databases, data archaeology, data dredging and intelligent data analysis. We define data mining as:

> The efficient, semi-automated process of discovering non-trivial, implicit, previously unknown, potentially useful and understandable information from large, historical and disparate data sets.

The move from hierarchical and network databases to relational databases, among other advantages, led to an abstraction of data retrieval away from the need for procedural descriptions of the data retrieval. Data mining can be envisaged as a further abstraction where the user no longer needs to be as exact about the data he or she wants retrieved, as is the case in SQL. Instead the user is only required to define an abstract goal to be achieved based on the knowledge discovered. For example, a data mining query could be: 'I want to cross sell products to my existing customers.'

Knowledge discovered using data mining may be in the form of deviations from norms, rules associating different products or associations among customer characteristics and products, rules discriminating among different segments in the database or temporal trends.

The data stored in the database is only the tip of the 'iceberg of information' available from it (see Fig. 1.5). Contained implicitly within this data is knowledge about a number of aspects of business operations waiting to be harnessed and used for more effective business decision support. While database management systems (DBMSs) allow efficient access and manipulation techniques for the data they are not geared towards providing concise information in a form suitable for use in business decision support. The main reason for this is the fact that DBMS technologies have never been intended for decision support and such support was left to client software such as spreadsheets as well as query and reporting tools. We discuss these technologies in Chapter 2 and describe how they fall short of decision support requirements.

Figure 1.5
THE ICEBERG OF INFORMATION

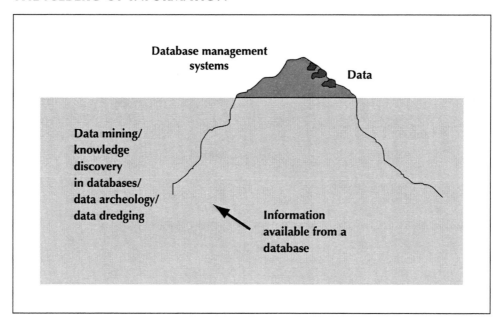

Data mining can be considered to be an inter-disciplinary field involving concepts from machine learning, database technology, traditional statistics, mathematics, uncertainty modelling, pattern recognition, high performance computing and visualisation among others.

As with any new technology transferred to industry from research laboratories, data mining does have a certain amount of hype associated with it and a number of vendors present it as the cure for all ills. Although such hype does produce short-term gains, it can only damage the long-term applicability of data mining. A prime example of a technology that suffered due to similar hype levels is expert systems. A rebirth of expert systems as knowledge-based systems has finally resulted in a less hyped but more successful technology. However, it has delayed its application within industry by almost a decade. The objective of this book is to provide a description of state-of-the-art data mining technologies available in the commercial environment. We hope to provide a realistic picture of what can be expected from the technology, and what is more hype than reality with respect to data mining.

1.4   THE CONTRIBUTION TO YOUR BUSINESS

We earlier discussed the changing needs of industry. Today any business intending to remain competitive requires information. Data warehousing, OLAP and data mining allow you to achieve the goal of gaining timely and high-quality information about your business.

Data warehouses are intended to provide high-quality data for analysis by OLAP and data mining software. Present operational database systems have failed in efficiently providing consistent, high-quality data for purposes of analysis. While we do not take a data warehouse to be a necessary precondition for data mining, to have a warehouse in place before carrying out data mining clearly is a beneficial situation. We discuss data warehousing objectives in greater detail in section 2.3.2.

OLAP is the term given to software that provides capabilities for analysing mutli-dimensional data, providing the data analysts with tools such as slice and dice, drill down, roll-up, rotation, etc. OLAP tools allow manual analysis for deviation detection and creation of trend hypotheses. Such tools are very useful from the point of view that they provide techniques to the data analyst with which they are familiar. OLAP, however, does not allow the discovery of totally unexpected information as does data mining, as it is directed by the data analyst who subconsciously uses biases that steer the analysis away from totally unexpected discovery.

Data mining techniques are semi-automated and, though they allow the user to provide some directionality, they can discover new and interesting information that is completely unexpected to the user. However, data mining is not a single-button top-management operation. It is a process that requires expertise in the domain and data as well as in data mining. In Chapter 4 we describe this process in greater detail. Though much progress has been made in the area, it is still very much an evolving, young technology with an ultimate goal of providing 'single-button' functionality. However, data mining has already been used successfully in a number of sectors, from retail to space exploration and manufacturing process improvement to healthcare modernisation, and success stories are available wherever you look. Today, data mining has become a necessity rather than the 'icing on the cake'.

1.5   SOME REPORTED DATA MINING SUCCESS STORIES

To give a flavour of what type of areas data mining is able to tackle successfully, a representative list of applications is discussed in this section.

Deciding whether a customer is a worthy credit risk, or if he or she might be a risky investment, is a crucial task for insurance companies and other financial organisations such as banks or building societies. Data mining has been used to provide such credit worthiness knowledge, causing such decisions to be made on a more informed, rather than 'gut feel', basis. British Telecom has employed data mining techniques to *assess creditability* of customers and applied the results discovered in various organisations in financial environments.

Many scientific models have been built in recent years to *predict stock market changes*. The Toronto Stock Market is one of the most modern in the world, with services such as market by price and fully electronic trading. Studies on the use of data mining techniques that consider inter-stock relationships have been carried out, and applied successfully on the Toronto Stock Market data.

Any *production environment* in the field of manufacturing relies heavily on minimal production interrupts and an appropriate ratio between maximal outcome and minimal faulty yields. (Semi-)automatic *diagnosis of faults* is an important field in such scenarios. Texas Instruments have used automated mining from their databases to track down the causes of misprocessing during semiconductor manufacturing. British Telecom partly replaced their existing expert system with appropriate data mining techniques based on neural networks to gain more accurate fault diagnosis in line cards used in digital switches. The result was a decrease in the amount of time and expertise required to build and maintain an adequate model of circuit functions.

One area of medicine that can greatly benefit from information is the *detection of causal information on diseases*. Data mining has been applied for the discovery of the causes of the deficiency disease scurvy. Knowledge discovered from historical observations of identical or similar cases simulated the explanation given to scurvy in seventeenth and eighteenth centuries. Another area where data mining has been applied is to provide the most appropriate *treatment strategy* for a patient. Data mining has been applied to infertility treatment, an area that varies in complexity, cost and incidence of patient complications. Instead of following the traditional approach of stepping from cheaper to more costly treatments, data mining techniques have been employed to discover patterns in data stored in the ovulation induction infertility database at the Jessop Hospital in Sheffield. The method identified characteristics of patients who are unlikely to become pregnant via ovulation induction treatment. Similar approaches can be applied in other medical fields and disciplines.

Data mining has also proved to be a useful technology for tackling some of the data intensive aspects of *fraud*. The Dutch police used tailored data mining tools to round up a ring of narcotics and drug peddlers, the Serious Fraud Office employed data mining techniques to highlight a mortgage fraud in the UK and British Telecom used similar techniques to locate fraud perpetuated against their telecommunication network.

Insurance companies make major losses with claims from *natural disasters*. Thus a system that could predict such natural disasters could prove very useful to the actuarial sector. Hurricane analysis has been carried out at the Travellers Insurance Company to forecast such natural disasters and estimate/minimise the costs of claims.

Large supermarket chains are using data mining techniques to *find patterns* in their 'shopping basket' data derived *from customer transactions* that highlight relationships among different products. Such knowledge can be used for product placement in stores, mutually exclusive special offers as well as better quantified and qualified purchasing from suppliers.

Any organisation has the objective to keep fixed costs as minimal as possible, and a major chunk of fixed costs are wages and salaries. In 1995, the British Army used data mining techniques on their payroll, personnel and pension data. As a consequence of the knowledge discovered, the *personnel infrastructure* has been *reduced* to a third of its original complexity.

Targeting potential customers is always confronted with the crucial trade-off between forgetting somebody and minimising the costs of such a campaign. One of the UK's biggest travel agencies Thomas Cook employed data mining to match the characteristics of prospective travellers and preferred holiday destinations to enable better target mailing. NBC provides advertisers with knowledge gained through the application of data mining on customer transactions on interactive TV. The information consists of qualified leads in terms of which customers to target, which channel to use or at what time of the day to advertise to achieve best returns.

Knowledge acquisition is one of the key steps in expert systems. A prototype of an expert system has been developed in the US recently to assess pre-term labour risks for pregnant women. Three databases containing data about pre-term and full-term deliveries have been processed using data mining techniques and the rules discovered have been used in the expert system. The TIGON expert system, under development at the University of Aberdeen, to detect and diagnose faults in an industrial gas turbine engine is also investigating the use of data mining for knowledge acquisition.

1.6 AUDIENCE AND OUTLINE OF TEXT

This book has three main audiences:

- management in various organisations;

- IT managers in data mining client organisations;

- data mining service providers.

First, it explains what data mining is and how it fits into the complex IT landscape. The aim is to provide management in various organisations with an idea of what data mining can do for them in strategic decision support. Second, it explains the various stages of how a data mining exercise should be conducted, whether it is a pilot or a full-scale project, for it to be successful in its objectives. Thus, it provides guidelines to managers in data mining client organisations as to how such a project should be managed. It also provides them with an idea of how much effort they can expect to be required on their part. It provides them with information on hidden costs that need to be taken into account when contemplating a data mining project and how data mining could affect other business processes within the organisation. Finally, it provides guidelines to data mining service providers as to a standard practice that they should employ to ensure successful implementation of their projects.

We have appended a collection of four case studies and a brief checklist-style market overview to put the book into a strong practical perspective. For reference purposes, we have also assembled a data mining glossary and further external sources of literature and Internet resources.

2

A historical perspective of data management

Data management started about three decades ago when data was stored in flat ASCII or EBCDIC operating system files without any information about the data. Often data had to be stored more than once across the organisation leading to inconsistencies and inefficiencies. There were no query languages, and any constraints or interrelationships among the entities were left to applications accessing the files. Database management systems were introduced in the late 1960s largely triggered by the Space Race. They provided these missing facilities and were based on either networks, hierarchies or (later) relations. Constraints such as data types, value ranges, dependencies or relationships among entities were provided and meta-data stored in data dictionaries. Later still, fourth generation languages were provided to ease application development. Within the last decade these systems have been extended to handle distributed and heterogeneous data, and thus more semantics about the interrelationships of different sites has had to be embedded. Richer modelling methods such as the semantic data model and object-oriented data models have now been developed and are making their mark in the industry.

State-of-the-art data management systems are platform-independent client-server solutions with active back-ends and visualised front-ends. In addition to user-friendly manual data-entering, these components allow automatic data generation, which leads to an enormous data volume increase. It is known that the amount of data stored electronically doubles every 20 months (Frawley *et al.*, 1991). The information hidden in both, the manually entered and the automatically generated data, is tremendous but the sheer size of the data makes its utilisation impossible.

So what have we been doing with all this data to date, and what will we do in the near future? The data flood will not stop, but we can slow down the increase in storage space required by using knowledge-based pre-processing techniques. That is, we will delete data, but not the information stored in the data. Thus, in addition to transaction and analysis orientated data processing, there will be a third component, which is to do with processing knowledge discovered from the data. This will solve quite a few problems outlined above, but it also introduces new obstacles:

• How do we know that the knowledge is correct?

• How can we manage knowledge in a similar way to how we handle data?

• What about data privacy aspects?

2.1   PROBLEMS AND ADVANTAGES

One of the major problems with the data collected by businesses is its state. First, as described in section 1.2, data collected by organisations is mainly distributed in legacy systems developed and maintained by different departments within the organisation. This data has slowly become inconsistent and inaccessible. The data is stored in a 'product-centred' way rather than a 'customer-centred' way. For example, a bank customer with a savings account, current account and Visa card has three different statuses in the bank as operational systems have been designed at the account level. However, for cross-sales, it would be necessary to find out for each customer which types of accounts he or she has. Such a link between the customer information and the different accounts often does not exist.

Another problem is that the data is noisy and incomplete. Though database structures are rich, the data population in these databases is low in fields that are important from a decision support perspective. For example, most banks today have a complete set of data that pertains to their customer transactions. However, customer details such as address, occupation, salary and number of dependants is incomplete and inaccurate. This is due to two main reasons. First, such information was seen by the bank's employees as an unnecessary waste of time with no apparent use and of inconvenience to the customer when opening the account. Therefore, fields that were not essential when entering information into the database were left empty. Second, the data itself is the kind that would change with time as customer circumstances change, and so such data needs to be updated. Up to now, this has not been regarded as an essential activity within the bank, thus the customer data is 'stale'. On the other hand, the transactional information is generated automatically by the system, for example whenever the customer uses an automatic telling machine (ATM).

However, the data exists and is stored electronically and so it should be possible, with varying degrees of difficulty, to make it consistent, informative and useful.

2.2 FROM TRANSACTION PROCESSING TO DECISION SUPPORT

Data mining builds on the foundation laid by the industry's transition from OLTP systems to data warehouses by providing tools to support operational strategy formulation. The need for data mining was felt due to the awareness that relational database management system (RDBMS) products were inappropriate for transforming data stored in OLTP applications into useful information. There are a number of specific reasons why RDBMSs are not suitable for business analysis (Codd et al., 1993) including:

- To make OLTP queries fast, RDBMS applications generally normalise the data into 50–200 tables. Though great for OLTP operations, this creates a huge overhead for business analysis applications as it means a large number of joins are required to access the data necessary for such applications.

- While parallel processing can be useful in table scans it offers very little performance enhancement for complex joins.

- SQL is not designed with common business needs in mind. There is no way of using standard SQL for retrieving information like 'the top 10 salespersons', 'bottom 20 per cent of customers', 'products with a market share of greater than 25 per cent' or 'the sales ratio of cola to root beer'.

- RDBMSs do not provide common data analysis tools like data rotation, drill-downs, dicing and slicing.

- To allow truly *ad hoc* end-user analysis, the database administrator should, ideally, index the database on every possible combination of columns and tables that the end user may ask for. This would create an unnecessary overhead for OLTP and query response times, as updates and deletions would need to be reflected in all the additional indexes.

- Locking models, data consistency schemes and caching algorithms are based on the RDBMS being used for OLTP applications where the transactions are small and discrete. Long-running, complex queries cause problems in each of these areas.

Thus, it soon became clear that current IT infrastructures would require an overhaul if operational data were to be made useful for decision support and strategic planning.

2.3   WHERE IS ALL THE DATA AT THE MINUTE?

2.3.1 Client-server database environments

With the rising amount of data and the need for more distributed data management, network traffic became unacceptably high. Instead of transferring all available information to a user's site (client), an alternative approach is to send only the requested data from a centralised storage (server). This system differs from traditional mainframe systems in that the user has his or her independent local work space, and contacts the server only if databases have to be queried or updated, i.e. each client component has its own processor.

The PC Webopaedia definition of client-server architecture is:

A network architecture in which each computer or process on the network is either a client or a server. Servers are powerful computers or processes dedicated to managing disk drives (file servers), printers (print servers) or network traffic (network servers). Clients are less powerful PCs or workstations on which users run applications. Clients rely on servers for resources, such as files, devices and even processing power.

Client-server applications may be two-tier or three-tier architectures (*see* Figs 2.1 and 2.2). In a three-tier architecture, the server application is further split up so that a *database server* is solely responsible for servicing the data requirements of an *application server* where the functional modules process the data. The client software normally consists of the *user interface* that runs on the user's computer.

Figure 2.1
A TWO-TIER CLIENT–SERVER ARCHITECTURE

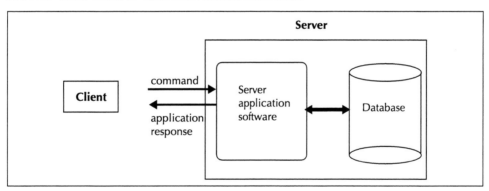

Figure 2.2
A THREE-TIER CLIENT–SERVER ARCHITECTURE

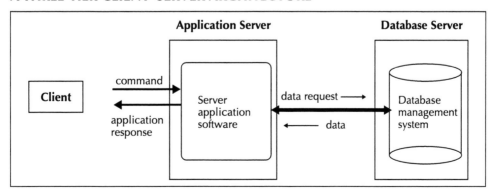

The advantages of client-server systems are obvious, which is reflected in the database industry having developed several products using client-server architectures. The underlying philosophy 'send a query and wait for the result' leads to less network traffic than any on-line system. Central data storage simplifies database integrity and security aspects. Additionally, database management tasks of an application (e.g. backups) are offloaded to the server. Also, hardware requirements are minimised in that a powerful server can satisfy numerous connected poorly equipped PCs or even dumb terminals.

But, in order to fully exploit a client-server architecture, not only is the distribution of database management required, but also that of data and application processing. Also, interoperability with other systems has been found awkward with initial client-server database systems. A more sophisticated approach is known as an enterprise database, where three-tier architectures represent clients, the data itself and shareable business information. Business information is often modelled as business objects or rules, and communication across applications and platforms is implemented through distributed information mechanisms such as CORBA or OLE. Another protocol which has been become the *de facto* standard in multi-database access is Open Database Connectivity (ODBC) from Microsoft (Sigmore *et al.*, 1995). Instead of developing a special method for every database which has to be used, only calls to the ODBC interface have to be set up. The actual connection is then handled by proprietary drivers. The advantages of this technique are its flexibility and openness. The drawbacks are often poor performance and limited operating system support (so far only Microsoft and some Unix platforms are supported as clients).

2.3.2 Data warehousing technology – 'laying the IT foundation for decision support'

Data warehouses (Inmon, 1992) are a new breed of database that are optimised for use in decision support (Red Brick Systems, 1995). They provide efficient access to corporate-wide data in a format that is understandable to decision makers using meta-knowledge built into the data loading algorithm that loads the data from the various legacy systems into the data warehouse.

Data warehouses principally integrate legacy systems within a corporation to provide an enterprise-wide view of the data necessary for decision making. This technology has become necessary due to the realisation on the part of large organisations that decisions about one business process cannot be made in complete isolation from other business processes within the enterprise. For example, large financial organisations may have different sections of their marketing departments maintaining their own customer data based around different products. The individual product-centred customer databases often do not link in together. While such a situation may be fine from a day-to-day operational perspective, clearly from a decision support perspective a much more beneficial situation would be a customer-centred database where the same customer identification number is used to identify all the different products bought by each customer.

Also, most large corporations have operational data in production systems that is unreliable and disparate, making it difficult to integrate or extract for analysis purposes. This data can also cause anomalies in data mining results. Thus the implementation of a data warehouse consists of the acquisition of data from multiple internal and external sources (of the corporation), the cleansing of this data, its management and integration into a central, integrated repository, the automatic updating of summary information in the warehouse based on the new data, the provision of access, and the provision of reporting and analysis tools to interpret selected data converting it into information to support managerial decision-making processes. Data warehouse architecture is summarised in Fig. 2.3.

Production or OLTP databases are not suitable for such decision support activities, as queries for decision support are normally complex and could span over 25 or more tables within an OLTP database. This is because OLTP databases were created with a view to optimising the performance of the OLTP operations and to reduce the amount of redundant information in the database. Joining these tables and producing a result would be very inefficient as join operations are computationally the most expensive database operation, especially when they are created in *ad hoc* queries not optimised by adding indices to the tables accessed. Also, most OLTP databases are being used to their limits and cannot, therefore, support such computationally expensive queries. Historical data is normally stored in backup storage devices and cannot be accessed. Such data, though not important for OLTP applications, is essential for trend analysis. Also, data stored in OLTP applications is not stored in formats that are understandable to the decision makers and would need a data expert to convert it into a format that is. During the loading of data from OLTP systems to the data warehouse, data is reformatted to make it available in terms of business concepts easily interpreted by decision makers.

Figure 2.3
ARCHITECTURE OF A DATA WAREHOUSE

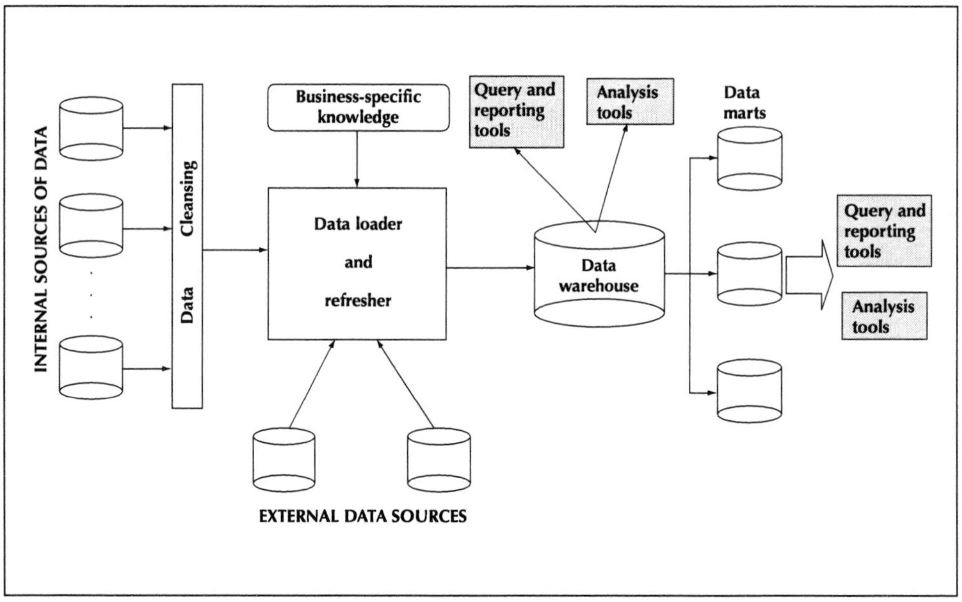

A related term is that of data marts. These, too, are databases designed to provide managers with easy access to data required for strategic decision making. Whereas a data warehouse combines databases across an entire enterprise, data marts are usually smaller and focus on a particular subject or department. Some data marts – called dependent data marts – are subsets of larger data warehouses (*see* Fig. 2.3).

Table 2.1 summarises the differences between OLTP and data warehouses in terms of their usage. It is clear from this that data warehouses require special methods for joins and data retrieval, e.g. STAR indexes and joins (Red Brick Systems, 1995), data loading and new query tools supporting common decision support operations.

Table 2.1
OLTP VS DATA WAREHOUSES

OLTP systems	Data warehouses
Data source generally human users through data entry screens	Data source normally legacy systems requiring automatic loading algorithms
Pre-defined queries	Ad hoc queries
Optimised retrieval paths	Complex retrievals
Small query results	Large query results
Frequent updates	Batch, infrequent updates

However, in a recent survey of data warehousing projects (*Conspectus*, 1996) it was reported that while most warehousing projects meet the users' requirements of data quality and integration, the ability to analyse and convert the data into information has been a major disappointment. Data mining and other data analysis tools attempt to provide this ability to convert data into information to the data warehouse user. According to Charles Bonomo, Vice-President of Advanced Technologies at J. P. Morgan, a large financial organisation in the US, 'One of the primary justifications for implementing a data warehousing solution is having a data mining tool in place that can access the data within it.' The most logical consequence is to integrate data mining technology as a central part of the data warehousing philosophy, without limiting any of the existing functionality.

2.3.3 Multi-dimensional databases

In section 2.2 we discussed some of the shortcomings of the relational model in providing analytical support to decision makers. A solution is the use of multi-dimensional database (MDD) servers that are a natural server database extension to the spreadsheet model. Unlike spreadsheets, however, the MDD server is not limited to two dimensions and is a more natural model for use by data analysts.

Data is multi-dimensional in nature and it is easier for data analysts to visualise it in such a way rather than as a set of two-dimensional tables which is the view taken by relational databases. While relational views can give the impression that all the data lies in one two-dimensional table, most RDBMSs do not support the construction of multi-dimensional views. Thus, it is up to the user to map their multi-dimensional world (data as well as operations) onto the two-dimensional relation.

MDD servers are designed specifically to handle complex queries that are commonplace in data analysis. As MDD servers are implemented specifically for OLAP which is carried out most effectively on historical data, MDD databases normally support a time dimension. Direct support for a time dimension makes MDD servers even more intuitive for decision makers.

2.4   THE FUTURE: WHAT CAN WE DO WITH ALL THAT DATA?

As outlined throughout the chapter, we have the pleasant circumstance to be equipped with vast amounts of data stored in various types of database systems. We also have the advantage of having mechanisms to access all the data and getting as much information as we want out of the data, as long as we know what the data is about. Knowing what the data is about is the crucial point in the up-to-date database world. We may find ourselves drowning in a flood of data and lose track of what data is actually available. This scenario becomes even worse with data generated automatically by logging facilities, search engines, transaction protocols, expert systems and so forth.

A promising perspective to this dilemma is that the data itself becomes less important; what is relevant is the information hidden in the data.

And this is exactly the main objective of data mining: 'finding previously unknown, potentially useful knowledge' (Fayyad *et al.*, 1996). We can go a step further and sketch a scenario in which all the relevant knowledge has been discovered, so it would be feasible to delete existing data and store only this knowledge.

But, this novel approach also brings a few unsolved problems and risks. Data itself is of an absolute, objective nature, knowledge is not. Who decides (and how) what knowledge is useful? How do we store knowledge appropriately? How do we maintain knowledge? What about privacy aspects of the discovered knowledge? And so forth.

As so often with revolutionary techniques in science, we end up in a trade-off where it has to be decided whether the profit from the new technology is worth more than the problems and risks coming with it. Data mining is definitely a potential candidate for such a trade-off, and appropriate technologies have to be incorporated to guarantee that it does not become a short-term buzzword, as happened to expert systems in the mid 1980s.

3

Related disciplines

Due to the limitations of pure database systems based on query languages such as SQL and fourth generation languages in building applications and front-end decision support tools, various tools have been developed to overcome these deficiencies. Disciplines related to data mining are mainly concerned with aspects of interpreting the data, analysis of its contents and visualising information retrieved.

In this chapter we discuss a number of disciplines related to data mining. It is important to differentiate between these and data mining so as to define the boundaries of what is encompassed by the term 'data mining'.

3.1   DATABASE REPORTING TOOLS

Database reporting tools were originally designed to provide lists derived from databases and data files. The outcome is usually based on queries performed against the data source and the report generator is used as a formatting tool for the resulting data. Additionally, grouping, summarising and other simple aggregation functionality is provided to allow the generation of high-level printouts.

With increasing user requirements, those tools have become more powerful and have been extended to provide basic statistical analysis functions, primitive visualisation of data through charts or graphs and proprietary macro languages. Recently, more and more functionality borrowed from OLAP (*see* section 1.2 and section 3.4) has been embedded in up-to-date database reporting tools, such as drill-down and roll-up operations, slicing and dicing, sub-reports for multi-dimensional views or cross-dimensional operations.

Also, report generators have been smoothly implemented as an essential part of data warehouses (*see* section 2.3.2). The next logical step is the support for presenting discovered knowledge from a data mining tool in a user-specific way. Techniques include natural language creation derived from discovered rules, visualisation of found clusters and sequences or tabulation of numeric knowledge.

3.2   STATISTICAL DATA ANALYSIS

The main purposes of statistics are to describe or summarise data, known as descriptive statistics, and to make inferences about a larger population of which the data is representative, usually referred to as inferential statistics (McClean and Scotney, 1996).* Both disciplines play a major role in various data mining techniques.

The objective of describing observations is to determine the type of data that has been collected. The concept is similar to attributes and their types in databases. Categorical variables involve putting individuals into categories (Fig. 3.1). Categorical variables may be nominal (e.g. red, green, purple) or ordinal. Ordinal variables themselves may be ordered categories (good, better, the best) or rank variables (first, second, third). Quantity variables are either discrete, i.e. countable (1 child, 2 children, 3 children), or continuous, i.e. measurable (6ft 3in, 6ft 4½in, 5ft 10¼in). This kind of modelling of real-world observations is important for representing data as a preparatory step for discovering knowledge.

Figure 3.1
TYPES OF STATISTICAL VARIABLES

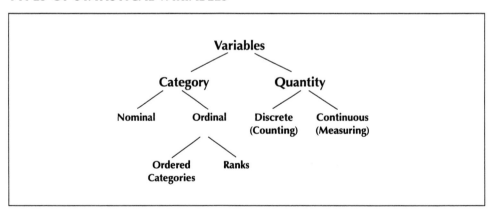

---

*   We only sketch the very basics of statistics to show its influence in data mining. More detailed information about the area can be found in any subject-related popular scientific treatise, or, for advanced techniques, consult available research material.

The objectives of *summarising* data are to represent the described observations in a useful format (using tables or diagrams/charts), and to quantify important features facilitating appropriate measures. Well-known measures for showing distributions are averages (mode, mean, median) and measures of dispersion (range values and standard deviation). To describe the shape of asymmetrical distributions various normalisation techniques have been developed to show proportions of populations between any two values.

Inferential statistics, also known as hypothesis testing, is mainly concerned with the generalisation, analysis, interpretation and prediction of the described observations. From the observed samples we can almost be sure that the data is neither complete nor fully accurate (similar to real-world databases). A technique that can handle such data is standard error calculation to generalise collected distributions. Mapping this concept onto data mining can be very powerful if data with null values and incorrect contents has to be mined. To compare originally incompatible distributions and proportions (discovered knowledge), statistics provides a battery of significance tests, such as null hypothesis, alternative hypothesis, chi-square values (x^2) and correlation coefficients. These techniques are often used to find associations among entities in databases (*see* section 5.1.1). For predicting values based on found associations, various regression techniques can be employed, depending on the type of variables, e.g. linear regression for quantity data, or log-linear modelling for category data.

In addition to criticism about statistics in general ('never use statistics when you know what you are talking about'), statistics also falls short of some goals of data mining. First, statistics is ill-suited for nominal and structured data types that are common in real-world databases. Second, statistics is totally data driven and does not provide techniques for incorporating domain or prior knowledge (*see* section 4.4). Third, the process of statistical data analysis requires expert user guidance. Last, the results from statistical analysis are difficult to interpret and are overwhelming to non-statisticians.

Various statistics packages have been developed over the last two decades, providing quite a complex battery of supported tools, techniques and methodologies. Recently, connections to database systems have become a standard feature of such packages, usually realised through Microsoft's ODBC interface (Sigmore *et al.*, 1995), to guarantee product-independent data access. Also, the integration of machine learning paradigms into statistical tools is becoming more common. For example, SAS now has rule induction and neural network components. We view these as positive developments. While they blur the distinction between these different disciplines, we believe it is to the advantage of the end-user of these tools. The real power of statistical techniques will almost certainly be unleashed through their use in an overall data mining framework as opposed to being considered as an alternative technology to data mining.

3.3   MACHINE LEARNING TOOLS

Learning from data has been an area of interest to machine learning enthusiasts since the 1970s. Over the past two decades machine learning research has matured with the development of a number of sophisticated techniques based on different models of human learning and reasoning. Learning by example, cased-based reasoning, learning by observation, neural networks, genetic algorithms and Bayesian belief networks are some of the most popular learning techniques which have been used to create the ultimate learning machine.

The main factor that distinguishes data mining from machine learning is that it is about learning from existing real-world data rather than data generated particularly for the learning tasks. Since in data mining data sets are large, efficiency and scalability of algorithms are important. As mentioned earlier the data from which data mining algorithms learn knowledge is already existing real-world data. Therefore, typically the data contains plenty of missing values as well as noise and it is not static, i.e. it is prone to updates. However, as the data is stored in databases, efficient methods for data retrieval are available that can be used to make the algorithms more efficient. Also, domain knowledge in the form of integrity constraints is available that can be used to constrain the learning algorithm's search space.

In summary, machine learning algorithms form the basis for most data mining tools. However, to make them suitable to handle real-world data mining problems, appropriate extensions have to be added to these techniques.

3.4   ON-LINE ANALYTICAL PROCESSING

Complex statistical functionality has never been intended to be accommodated within RDBMSs. Providing such functionality was left to user-friendly end-user products such as spreadsheets or statistical packages which are supposed to act as front-ends to the RDBMS. Though statistics packages and related tools have provided a certain amount of functionality required by business analysts, none address, to any great extent, the need for analysing the data according to its multiple dimensions. Any product that intends to provide such functionality to business analysts must provide the following features to allow adequate statistical data analysis:

- access to many different types of files;

- creation of multi-dimensional views of the data;

- experimentation with various data formats and aggregations;

- definition and visual animation of new information models;

- application of summations and other formulae to these models;

- operations such as drilling down, rolling up, slicing and dicing and rotation of consolidation paths;

- generation of a wide variety of reports, charts and diagrams.

On-line analytical processing (OLAP) is the name given by Codd *et al.*,
1993) to the technologies that attempt to address these user
requirements. E. F. Codd defined OLAP as 'the dynamic synthesis,
analysis and consolidation of large volumes of multi-dimensional data'
(*see* Table 3.1 and Fig. 3.2). Another definition given by Pendse and
Creeth (1995) is '**F**ast **A**nalysis of **S**hared **M**ulti-dimensional **I**nformation'
(FASMI). They have given further clarification of the five terms in the
definition. 'Fast' refers to the response times expected from OLAP
systems. They suggest an upper limit of 20 seconds on the most complex
of queries made by the user. The motivation behind this is that if the
queries take significantly longer, the user is likely to get distracted and
lose his or her chain of thought resulting in decreased effectiveness of
the OLAP system. 'Analysis' means that the system should provide the
tools for analysis in an intuitive form to the user. 'Shared' refers to
the fact that the system should be able to handle multiple users and
should provide for all security and concurrency requirements.
'Multi-dimensional' is a key requirement as users think in a
multi-dimensional way and, therefore, all their queries are constructed
in a multi-dimensional environment. Thus, the system should handle
multi-dimensionality along with any hierarchies on the dimensions as
defined by the user. Finally, 'Information' is all the data and derived
knowledge available from the data. Thus, the FASMI definition covers
the performance and facilities expected from OLAP systems.

Figure 3.2
OLAP'S MULTI-DIMENSIONAL VIEW OF DATA

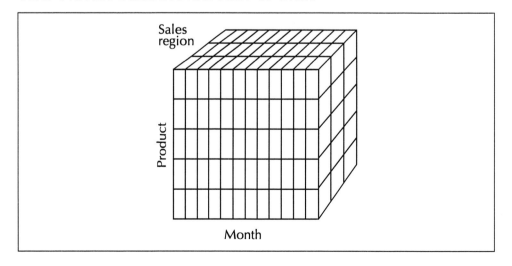

Table 3.1
CODD'S 12 RULES/REQUIREMENTS OF AN OLAP SYSTEM

Multi-dimensional conceptual view	As business analysts are used to thinking of the business in a multi-dimensional way, the system must provide facilities for preserving this view and defining it in a multi-dimensional environment, rather than requiring the view to be defined in terms of two-dimensional, flat relations as is the case with the relational model.
Transparency	The source of the data being analysed should be transparent to the user – whether the data source is distributed or heterogeneous should not be the concern of the user.
Accessibility	The OLAP system should be able to map its conceptual schema onto the underlying relational as well as legacy databases in other formats and perform the necessary conversions.
Consistent reporting performance	As the number of dimensions increases, there should be no visible degradation in the performance of the system. If this is not the case, the user would tend to reduce the number of dimensions so as to achieve acceptable performance, possibly trading off the accuracy of the analysis.
Client-server architecture	OLAP systems should have a client-server architecture with the server application having the capability to serve multiple users concurrently.
Generic dimensionality	All the dimensions should be equivalent in terms of the manipulation capabilities provided by the OLAP server.
Dynamic sparse matrix handling	Normally data in databases, when stored multi-dimensionally, results in a sparse n-dimensional hypercube. An OLAP system should be able to utilise this sparseness to enhance its storage and manipulation capabilities.
Multi-user support	The OLAP server should be able to handle multiple users concurrently without visible degradation in the performance.

Unrestricted cross-dimensional operations	Analysis operations and data manipulation should be unrestricted and uninhibited by any relationship between the dimensions that are associated with the data cell in the multi-dimensional representation of the data.
Intuitive data manipulation	Data manipulation operations like zooming in and out of consolidation paths should be intuitive to the analyst and possibly configurable to the user's needs.
Flexible reporting	Reporting of the results of the analysis should be flexible and intuitive.
Unlimited dimensions and aggregation levels	Aggregation levels in any consolidation path defined by the user and dimensions within the analytical model should not be limited as these limit the analysis capabilities of the system and are the most important motivation behind the development of the OLAP tool.

A number of extensions to these OLAP requirements have been suggested since then (Buytendijk, 1995), including: support for multiple arrays, time series analysis, OLAP joins, procedural language and development tools, database management tools, object storage, integration of functionality, subset selection, detail drill-down, local data support, incremental database refresh and an SQL interface. The back-end to an OLAP system, often referred to as the OLAP server, may be either a data warehouse (*see* section 2.3.2) or a multi-dimensional database (*see* section 2.3.3).

4

The data mining process

In this chapter we discuss the data mining process (*see* Fig. 4.1). In Chapter 1 we described how data mining technologies have become a necessity in the present climate of 'info-centric' economies. However, a data mining project, if not carried out with great care and following correct procedures, may result in resources being spent without any useful knowledge being generated, i.e. it may turn out to be a liability as opposed to an asset. Thus, we now discuss how a data mining project needs to be approached.

The usual seed for a data mining project is the need for information on the part of the decision makers to respond to moves made by their competitors. Thus, the identification of a problem requiring a well-informed solution is the starting point of the data mining process. We shall use the following example, wherever possible, from the manufacturing sector to illustrate the various stages of the process.

Figure 4.1
THE DATA MINING PROCESS

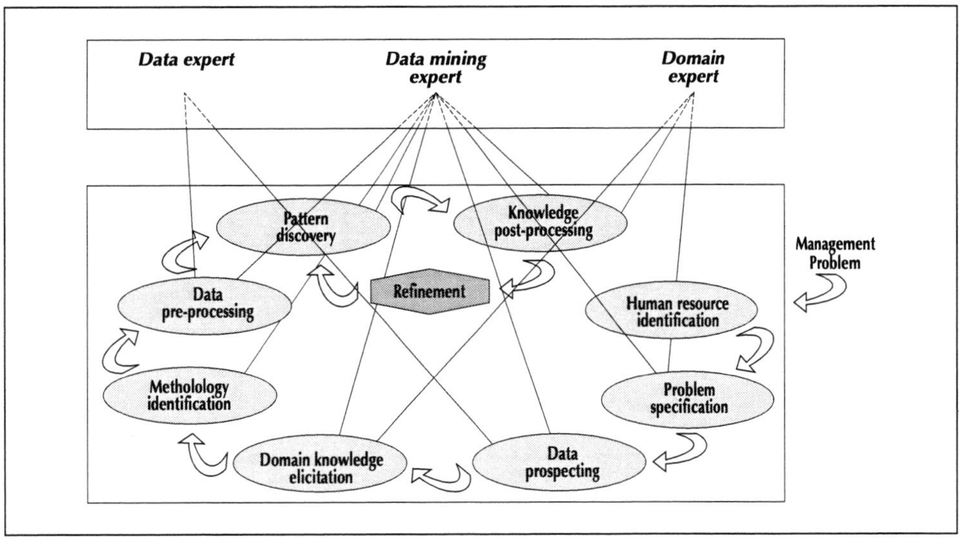

Example: Consider the case of a large manufacturing company. The company incurs large losses due to faults in their manufactured products that are undoubtedly caused by variations in their manufacturing environment. This is the problem identified at top-management level and they want to investigate a possible solution to the problem using data mining.

4.1   HUMAN RESOURCE IDENTIFICATION

After a problem has been identified at the management level of an organisation human resource identification is the first phase of the data mining process. In most real-world data mining problems the human resources required are in the following areas:

- domain expertise

- data expertise

- data mining expertise.

Normally, data mining is carried out in large organisations where the prospect of finding a domain expert who is also an expert in the data stored by the organisation is rare. For example, in a large bank, the domain expert would belong to the marketing department while the data expert will probably belong to the IT department. The data mining expert would normally belong to an organisation outside the bank employed by the bank for the purpose of solving the identified problem using data mining. It is very important that these human resources are brought together early in the process as any project that does not bring together this expertise right at the beginning will very likely encounter problems later on.

A typical scenario in an organisation is that data mining is received with greater enthusiasm by the IT department than by the domain experts. As a result, the project starts with data mining and data expertise, but the domain expertise is half-hearted as the domain experts are sceptical about the usefulness of the new technology. The domain experts view their efforts in the project as additional rather than central to their work. Therefore, it is important for IT professionals with the organisation to promote and increase awareness within their organisation of the benefits of data mining, before commencing on the project.

In our manufacturing example, the data expert would belong to the IT department responsible for production databases. The domain expert would belong to the production department and would ideally have an understanding of the overall production process.

> **Step 1:** Identify a motivated data and domain expert

4.2   PROBLEM SPECIFICATION

Problem specification is the second phase of the data mining process. During this stage, the domain and data mining experts map out the various components of the business solution required as an output from the data mining process. It is critical for data mining experts to clarify in their mind what type of data mining goals are involved in the solution and for that reason it is imperative that they gain a clear understanding of the problem at hand. The problem is disassembled into smaller tasks and those tasks that require a data mining solution are focused upon. We refer to these tasks as *data mining tasks* (DMTs).

Returning to our manufacturing example, a complete solution to the problem identified would consist of a number of components. First, the company would need to collect data about each manufactured product as it passes through the manufacturing process. This could be done preferably by putting automated data acquisition systems in place that collect various manufacturing parameter values, or by manual recording. Next, large variations in the manufacturing environment causing deviations in manufacturing quality need to be detected. Once these are identified, the patterns that identify ideal manufacturing conditions need to be discovered and verified. Finally, the use of these patterns needs to be automated to monitor the manufacturing processes on-line, and techniques for introducing corrective measures need to be identified and implemented. The two DMTs involved here are 'detecting deviations in manufacturing performance' and 'discovery of manufacturing performance patterns'.

The problem specification stage may be subdivided into the identification of the DMTs and their mapping onto data mining goals, and the identification of the end user of the knowledge to be discovered as a result of data mining.

4.2.1 Task identification

During this sub-process, each DMT is identified as a particular type of *data mining goal* (DMG). A number of different DMGs have been identified in literature, the main ones being discovery of associations, classification, sequential pattern discovery, discovery of characteristics, clustering or data segmentation, deviation detection, regression and temporal modelling. These goals are defined in greater detail in section 5.1. Different data mining methodologies (*see* section 5.2) are used to tackle each of these DM goals. Therefore, identifying the DMG that the DMT falls into is imperative for the success of a data mining project. Note that we are taking for granted that the user has some idea of the problem he or she is trying to solve. In most cases this is a fair assumption as 'pure discovery' completely data driven is rare. Several discovery methodologies are discussed in detail in section 5.2.

Returning to our manufacturing example, the first DMT, i.e. 'detecting deviations in manufacturing performance', clearly has a deviation detection DMG (*see* section 5.1.6). The second DMT, i.e. 'discovery of manufacturing performance patterns', has a classification DMG (*see* section 5.1.2).

Step 2: Identify the data mining tasks in the problem and map them onto their data mining goals

---

4.2.2 User identification

The second part of the problem specification phase is to identify the ultimate user of the knowledge. Clearly if the knowledge discovered is to be used by a human, it must be in a format that the user can

understand and is used to. However, if data mining is only a small part
of a larger project and the output from data mining is to be interpreted
by a computerised system (e.g. a decision support system), the format
of the discovered knowledge will have to strictly adhere to the format
expected by the computerised system.

There are a great many knowledge representation techniques, each
with a different level of perspicuity (Fig. 4.2), the most common types
used are rules (if … then … else statements), decision trees
(hierarchical representation), Bayesian belief networks (acyclic graphs)
and neural networks (black box). It is important to note that one is
often confronted with a trade-off between the perspicuity of the
knowledge representation technique and the ability of the data mining
methodology (*see* section 5.2) to tackle the problem at hand.

Figure 4.2
THE KNOWLEDGE REPRESENTATION SCALE OF PERSPICUITY

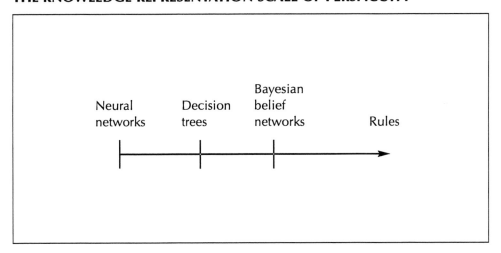

In our manufacturing example the patterns discovered in the
'discovery of manufacturing performance patterns' DMT need to be
understandable to the human domain expert who can suggest
corrective measures that need to be implemented in each case where
the pattern leads to a non-ideal manufacturing environment. Common
knowledge representations for classification patterns are rules,
decision trees and neural networks. As neural networks do not
represent knowledge in a form intelligible to humans, the options
available to us in this case are decision trees and rules. Knowledge

discovered from the deviation detection DMG will be used as an input to the classification DMG. Therefore, its representation must be in a way that can be handled by the data mining methodology used for the classification DMT.

Step 3: Identify the user of the output of the data mining tasks and the required knowledge representation scheme

---

4.3   DATA PROSPECTING

Data prospecting is a critical phase of the process. It consists of analysing the state of the data required for solving the problem at hand. There are four main considerations within this stage:

• What are the relevant attributes?

It is important to include within the data set all data attributes that could be related to the problem at hand and not just those that are 'relevant' according to the domain expert as the domain expert may be using biases that are not necessarily entirely justified. *It is important to let the data speak for itself as opposed to using any user bias that is not fully justified.* Only the data attributes that have obvious values associated with the problem at hand should be removed from the data set. For example, if we want to discover the characteristics of customers of an insurance product that is aimed at house owners there is no point in including the data attribute 'house status' as it will always have the value 'owner'. During this stage the data mining expert, having gained a clear understanding of the problem at the problem specification stage, and the data expert work closely to map the DMT onto the data sources modelling the business.

• Is the data required electronically stored and accessible?

Sometimes data is still maintained manually or archived in 'IT-ancient' media. For physical, legal or intellectual property reasons, data might not be accessible, which often leads to time-consuming negotiations with the responsible administrator.

- Are the required data attributes well populated?

Data stored in OLTP systems often suffers from low population of attributes that are considered unimportant from the OLTP application's point of view. Thus, while the database schema may be rich enough for data mining to be effective, the population of these attributes may prohibit useful data mining to be carried out. The reason for this under-population of attributes can be seen from the following example. Consider a staff member at a bank that is opening an account for a new customer. As attributes such as number of dependants seems to be unimportant from the bank's OLTP application, the clerk saves the new customer the trouble of filling in the information. But what about the potential use of that information in decision support? Thus, the root cause of the under-population of attributes is the ignorance on the part of staff on the possible usefulness of the data in applications other than the one that is generating the data.

- Is the data distributed, heterogeneous, stored in legacy systems or centrally stored?

If the data is heterogeneous, the semantic inconsistencies have to be determined and whether they can be accounted for by the data expert or whether they need to be ascertained before the data can be used for discovering knowledge for decision support. For example, three computerised systems within a hospital in Northern Ireland – the Patient Administration System, the Laboratory System and the Radiology System – contain different aspects of a patient's previous medical history but they do not contain a common key with which this information can be aggregated. Clearly, such inconsistencies must be removed if data mining is to be performed on the patient data to discover healthcare patterns.

It is important to investigate any useful, externally available data too. Clearly, in the manufacturing sector external data will not be very useful as most manufacturing processes are localised and specially designed or tailored to each individual manufacturer. However, externally procured data can prove to be very useful in sectors like finance, where data sets like Acorn and Mosaic that provide general lifestyle patterns based on geographical location, and other data sets that provide information such as relative depravation of different areas, can prove very useful. Once again we must consider any semantic inconsistencies that may exist between this externally procured data and the organisation's privately owned internal data. A typical inconsistency between Acorn and internal data is the fact that Acorn uses census enumeration districts as their geographical location indicators whereas most organisations would use postcodes.

Returning to the manufacturing example, the process of manufacturing involves four different phases – say A, B, C and D. On investigating the state of the data acquisition at each of the phases, it is found that data is acquired for phases A and B using automated acquisition systems, data is collected manually for phase C, while no data is collected on phase D. Data from phases A and B is stored in separate databases; however, both used the same key field, a unique product identifier, so collating the information from the two database is straightforward. The data from phase C, on the other hand, is stored on paper and the unique product identifier is not recorded along with the data, only a time stamp for when the product arrived at phase C.

Note that during this phase we are only documenting the data and possible problems with it. Solving any incompatibilities is part of the data pre-processing phase.

> **Step 4:** Identify the relevant data for each data mining task and determine its accessibility and usefulness: *Let the data speak for itself as opposed to using any user bias that is not fully justified.*

4.4   DOMAIN KNOWLEDGE ELICITATION

During this stage of the data mining process, having identified the data that is relevant to the problem being tackled, the data mining expert now attempts to elicit any domain knowledge that the domain expert may be interested in incorporating into the data mining process. The domain knowledge must be verified for consistency before proceeding to the next stage of the process.

Domain knowledge is useful within data mining in a number of different ways as follows:

- It can make patterns in data more visible. Data stored in OLTP databases may be at too detailed a level to discover meaningful patterns from it. For example, domain knowledge that provides a hierarchical generalisation of the attribute values in the database can make patterns more visible (*see* section 4.4.1).

- It can be used to constrain the search space of the data mining exercise. Attribute dependencies (*see* section 4.4.3), syntactic constraints, i.e. specification of attributes of interest, and/or intentional attributes, i.e. a mathematical formula involving attributes in the data set that are more relevant to the discovery task from a domain-specific viewpoint, may be defined by the user to constrain the search space.

- It can provide information known to the domain expert that is not available from the data itself. These may be constraints due to the discovery environment. For example, consider a geographically distributed database from which knowledge is being discovered. Information that the data in the database at location 1 is not as reliable as the data stored at location 2 needs to be incorporated into the discovery process to get correct results.

- It can make the discovery of knowledge more efficient. The efficiency of data mining algorithms is increased by the constraining of the search space as described above.

- It can be used to filter out obvious knowledge by using a knowledge-based approach to defining the 'interestingness' of knowledge. For example, if the domain expert was to provide a knowledge base containing his or her knowledge of the field, only knowledge that either contradicts or deviates greatly from this knowledge is deemed as being of interest to the user, reducing the human effort required for knowledge post-processing (*see* section 4.8).

Domain knowledge may be in the form of hierarchical generalisations of attribute values, rules that the domain expert is already aware of, attribute dependencies or rules of thumb used by the domain expert.

4.4.1 Hierarchical generalisation trees

Very often data stored in databases needs to be generalised in order to get meaningful or useful information. For example, finding rules that associate the date of birth of a particular customer with the car he drives is less useful than finding rules that associate an age bracket with a car type.

Figure 4.3
EXAMPLE OF A HIERARCHICAL GENERALISATION TREE

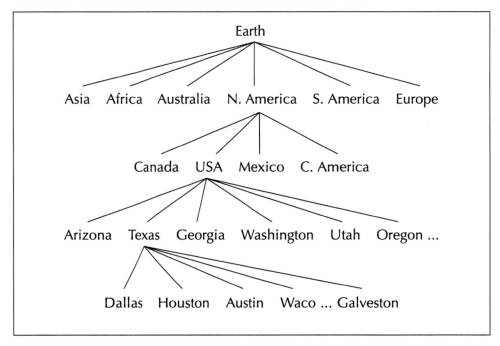

Hierarchical generalisation trees (HG-tree) are domain specific generalisations of attribute values that may be used to discover more general rules from the database. For example, consider the HG-tree in Fig. 4.3. The coarseness of the attribute increases as we move up from the lowest level of the tree. The lowest level represents the attribute values as stored in the database. A rule discovered for individual cities in Texas may not strike the user as a useful or interesting rule as it may not be supported by a large enough percentage of the database. However, if we were to generalise the rule to one that applies to Texas instead, the rule may prove to be more interesting.

4.4.2 Attribute relationship rules

Attribute relationship rules represent knowledge about the domain that the domain expert is aware of prior to the discovery. Such knowledge may be used to deal with missing information in the database or to filter out obvious knowledge during knowledge post-processing. An example of an attribute relationship rule is:

> *if Mortgage Customer = Yes*
> *then Account Average Balance in [10K, 15K] and Occupation =*
> *Professional*

The rule states that mortgage customers have an average account balance between £10 000 and £15 000 pounds and are in a professional occupation.

4.4.3 Attribute dependencies

Domain knowledge of this form describes interdependencies between attributes in the database being mined. For example, consider a hospital database with a laboratory results table with the following structure:

> *Result(PatientID, TestName, TestComponent, Result)*

Clearly, rules that include the *Result* field and not both *TestName* and *TestComponent* attributes are not useful rules. Thus, *Result* is dependent on *TestName* and *TestComponent*. Such domain knowledge is represented as follows:

(TestName, TestComponent) ⟶ *Result*

The advantage of incorporating such domain knowledge is the reduction in the number of rules discovered by eliminating rules that associate patient characteristics with the attribute *Result* if the *TestName* and *TestComponent* are not in the discovered rule as well.

4.4.4 Environment-based constraints

Often there are constraints on the discovery goal that are enforced by the environment in which the discovery is being carried out. For example, consider a database consisting of images of Mars taken from two cameras on a spaceprobe. Features are extracted from images taken by each of the cameras and stored in two separate databases. Now suppose that one of the cameras took the photographs from a skewer angle than the other – clearly the features extracted from the images photographed by this camera would be less reliable than those taken by the other camera. Such information must be taken into account when discovering knowledge from these databases and making decisions on further probe missions.

More specific environment-based constraints also exist. In certain cases when the DMT at hand has a classification goal it is important to ascertain as to whether the cost of misclassification is the same for all the different classes. For example, consider the following case from the actuarial sector. The ABC motor insurance company has a customer database. The company would like to determine in advance as to which customers are likely to allow their policy to lapse and which customers are likely to renew. The goal here is to try and dissuade customers likely to lapse from doing so by offering them some additional incentives. Now, a misclassification can be of two types: the first type is when a customer likely to lapse is classified as a customer likely to renew and the second type is when a customer likely to renew is classified as a customer likely to lapse. Clearly, the cost of the first type of misclassification is much greater than that of the second. Thus, any classifier induced for this problem should minimise such misclassifications while still keeping the number of misclassifications of the second type as low as possible. Such circumstances result in an additional constraint on the final selection of the 'best' classification model (*see* section 4.8) formulated as:

$$Min(cost\_1 * number\_1 + cost\_2 * number\_2)$$

where, *cost_1* and *cost_2* are the respective costs of misclassification of types 1 and 2, and *number_1* and *number_2* are the number of misclassifications of types 1 and 2, respectively.

Another scenario is when some of the attributes in the data from which discovery is to be carried out have different costs of acquisition associated with them. For example, consider the following scenario in the medical sector. A patient database of cancer patients is to be mined to discover a classification model that predicts whether a patient should be treated with radiation or by oral medication. The database consists of a number of clinical observations and investigations concerning past patients. Clearly, different costs are associated with the acquisition of each of the clinical observations and investigations. For example, the mining system may discover the attribute biopsy as the best clinical attribute to differentiate between the two types of treatment. However, carrying out a biopsy can be painful and often unnecessary. Thus, it may be better to try and avoid carrying out a biopsy as much as is possible. Such biases must also be identified and provided as environment-based constraints to the mining system.

In the manufacturing example, misclassifying a bad manufacturing environment as a good environment is clearly more costly than when a good environment is classified as a bad one, as in the latter case the only cost will be a resetting of manufacturing parameters while in the former case large re-engineering costs will be incurred.

> **Step 5:** Identify attribute generalisations, attribute dependencies, environmental constraints and any knowledge about the domain known to domain experts

4.5   METHODOLOGY IDENTIFICATION

The main task of the *methodology identification* stage is to find the best data mining methodology to solve the specified mining problem. Data mining methodologies can be broadly classified into those based on traditional statistics, machine learning, visualisation and uncertainty, and those based on database techniques (*see* Fig. 4.4). Often a combination of methodologies is required to solve the problem at hand. For example, clustering or data segmentation may be required before the application of a classification algorithm. The most commonly used technologies are briefly described in section 5.2. The paradigm chosen for a given task depends on the type of information that is required, the state of the available data (accessed at the data prospecting stage), the problem at hand and the domain of the knowledge being discovered. For example, if an explanation of the discovered knowledge is required neural networks would clearly not be an appropriate methodology. The selected technique may influence the format of the input data, whose preparation is part of the following data mining step. For example, when using neural networks, data transformation may be required to map input data into the interval [0, 1], or when association rule induction is being used the data may need to be discretised or converted into a binary format depending on the association algorithm used. The success of this stage mainly depends on the experience and expertise of the data mining expert.

In the manufacturing example, the first DMT used visualisation and statistical techniques while the second DMT used rule induction.

> **Step 6:** Take the domain, format of input data, acquired domain knowledge and output requirements into account when deciding on the methodology to be used

Figure 4.4
DATA MINING METHODOLOGIES

```
                    ┌─────────────────────────────┐
                    │  Data Mining Methodologies  │
                    └─────────────────────────────┘
```

Traditional statistics	Machine learning techniques	Uncertainty based techniques	Database techniques
• Exploratory data analysis	• Rule induction	• Bayesian belief networks	• Set-oriented approaches
• Log-linear modelling	• Case-based reasoning	• Fuzzy logic	• Attribute-oriented induction
• Linear regression	• Genetic algorithms	• Rough sets	• Statistical databases
• Multivariate analysis	• Connectionist approaches	• Evidence theory	

```
                    ┌──────────────┐
                    │ Visualisation │
                    └──────────────┘
```

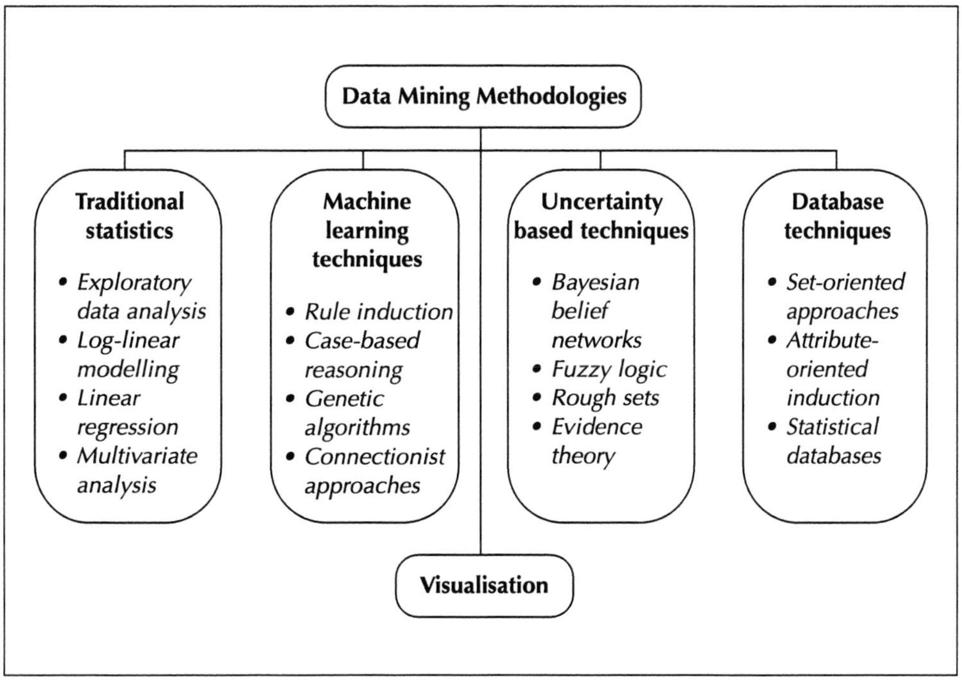

4.6   DATA PRE-PROCESSING

Depending on the state of the data this process may constitute the stage where most of the effort (sometimes as much as 80 per cent of the overall effort) of the data mining process is concentrated. Data pre-processing or scrubbing involves removing outliers in the data, data enrichment, predicting and filling in missing values, noise modelling, data dimensionality reduction, data quantisation, transformation, coding and heterogeneity resolution.

Unfortunately, this is an area that is least provided for by data mining vendors as many of them consider this stage to be part of data warehousing as opposed to data mining. However, the majority of data mining projects that the authors have been involved in have been in organisations that do not have a data warehouse or are in the process of implementing one, but want to run pilot studies in data mining in parallel to quantify the advantages of a full-fledged data mining system as part of their data warehouse. While there is specialised data scrubbing and cleansing software available in the market their costs prohibit their use especially in pilot studies and in organisations that are not contemplating a data warehouse. We would like to stress the fact that, *while having a data warehouse does help in data mining, under no circumstances is it a necessity* and great benefits can be reaped (at an additional cost!) by mining operational databases by collating data and cleansing it for the sole purpose of carrying out a data mining exercise.

Data pre-processing in data mining has often been considered the equivalent of the 'stick of dynamite' for the mining of ores. No pre-processing may result in the really useful knowledge remaining undiscovered. However, too much pre-processing (also known as over-pre-processing) may result in the discarding of the data in which the interesting knowledge is hidden. Thus, there is a balance required during pre-processing. This stage requires input from the data expert as well as the data mining expert. While the data expert can provide domain expertise about the data in terms of integrity constraints and the domain-dependent meanings of different attribute values, the data mining expert can base his or her decision to use different pre-processing techniques based on the knowledge provided by the data expert.

Outliers and noise in the data can skew the learning process and result in less accurate knowledge being discovered. They must be dealt with before discovery is carried out. Census data and other economic and lifestyle data based on geographic information can now be bought for enriching the data available from operational databases. For example, the Acorn and Mosaic data sets provide general lifestyle and economic factors based on geographical information. Thus, this data may be added to existing data in a customer base through mapping it onto a geographical information system. Missing values in the data must either be filled in or a methodology used that can take them into consideration during the discovery process to account for the incompleteness of the data model. Data dimensionality reduction is an important aid to improve the efficiency of the data mining algorithm as most have execution times that increase exponentially with respect to the number of attributes within the data set. Depending on the methodology chosen the data may need to be coded or discretised.

Returning to the manufacturing example, we noted during the data prospecting stage that the data required for the DMTs, identified in the problem specification stage, was stored in distributed, heterogeneous databases. As part of the data pre-processing stage a method is to be devised to link the distributed data sources from phases A and B to the data source from phase C. A good understanding of the production process would be required to develop a method for solving the problem by identifying a set of attributes within the data from phase C that would best substitute for the missing key attribute. Returning to the fact that no data is available on phase D of the manufacturing process, there are two possible ways of tackling this problem. The first is to install a data acquisition system on phase D of the process. The alternative would be to ignore the fact that the data is missing and to attempt to build a model based on the available data. We assume the latter option in our example.

We now discuss in greater detail various aspects of data pre-processing.

4.6.1 Noise and residual variation

A *deterministic domain* is one where a data set is available such that every outcome or class can be determined correctly based on the attributes available. Such a data set is said to be complete from the point of view of the DMG at hand.

Unfortunately, such domains are rare in the real world. Most domains are *non-deterministic* and data sets are *incomplete* resulting in varying degrees of uncertainty. Two different sources of this uncertainty exist. The first is that of *mismeasurement*, where values within the data set are erroneous due either to the source of the attribute value or to an error in entering the value into the database. This source of uncertainty is termed as *noise*. Note that missing values are also a form of noise. The second source of uncertainty concerns factors that occur in the domain that have not been recorded. While they do affect the outcome or class attribute, as they are not recorded as part of the data set they cannot be part of the model being induced and thus the variability in the class distribution cannot be explained completely. Such a data set is termed as being *incomplete* with respect to the DMG at hand and this source of uncertainty is termed as *residual variation.*

In our manufacturing example, having left out data on phase D from our data mining exercise, it is almost inevitable that we would have residual variation within our data unless, of course, phase D has no effect on the final outcome of the product – a highly unlikely scenario. However, given the data we have stored, we may still be in a position to discover a fairly accurate model, the performance of which would depend on how much the missing data contributes to the outcome of manufacturing.

4.6.2 Discovering outliers

An *outlier* is an unusually large or unusually small data point occurring in the data space. Outliers may be good or bad. A good outlier is a value that is occurring in the data because it occurs in the real world being modelled by the data and is a chance happening which, from a deviation detection point of view, is an interesting finding. Bad outliers are generally noise in the data and need to be removed before data mining is carried out as they may skew the learning algorithm and reduce the accuracy of the discovered knowledge. In general, it is safe to remove all outliers from the data as even the good outliers, if left within the data, will skew the learning algorithm. For example, a housing database being used to train a neural network to predict house prices may contain houses with extremely low prices compared to other houses with exactly the same attributes. There can be a number of reasons for this: unrecorded attributes may be causing residual variation (for example, the sale was a family sale or the area in which the house is has a high crime rate) or it may be noise in the data. In either case, the neural network, in its attempt to reduce the mean squared error of its predictions, will learn to underestimate the value of houses with those particular attributes.

Outliers, once removed, need to be analysed separately and the good outliers identified and stored as exceptions within the discovered knowledge base. Outliers may be identified using any of a number of exploratory data analysis techniques, for example the z-score or box plots.

4.6.3 Missing values

Missing values may appear in a data set for one of two reasons. The first is when the value has not been recorded. Techniques commonly used to fill in such missing values before induction range from using the modal value (for the class associated with the example) to inducing a decision tree to predict the missing values. However, empirical comparisons of these techniques have shown that none of the techniques apart from the use of distributions perform any better than the modal method.

The second reason for missing values is the fact that none of the attribute values are applicable due to the value of some other attribute. The method used to handle such missing data depends on the methodology being employed for pattern recognition. For example, for classification problems when inducing a decision tree, the only way round the situation is to not allow the attribute to be considered as the split attribute.

4.6.4 Data dimensionality reduction

Induction algorithms suffer in the presence of irrelevant attributes. Irrelevant attributes lead to larger and more complex knowledge structures and also reduce their predictive accuracy. Thus, techniques that identify the irrelevant attributes and remove them from the data set before the induction of the predictive model can be useful pre-processing tools.

A number of induction algorithms attempt to deal with the problem of irrelevant attributes directly. For example, induction of logical conjunctions (including decision trees) add or remove features from the concept description, non-symbolic methods like neural networks and Bayesian classifiers use weights to assign degrees of relevance to attributes while nearest neighbour approaches tend to ignore the issue of irrelevant attributes altogether. However, it has been shown that these algorithms can gain in accuracy and simplicity by employing techniques for the identification and removal of irrelevant attributes from the training data set prior to induction. Techniques that utilise measures such as Euclidean distance, for example nearest neighbour and other clustering techniques, are more susceptible to reduced accuracy due to the presence of irrelevant attributes.

4.6.5 Data coding and quantisation

Different data mining methodologies have different data input requirements and an important part of data pre-processing is to code the data into the required format. For example, algorithms for discovery of associations require the data to be categorical. Thus, continuous variables must be split into intervals. Such a quantisation can have a profound effect on the discovered knowledge and must be carried out carefully. Similarly, in the case of the use of neural networks, data may need to be coded (Bigus, 1996). Similar coding is required when using genetic algorithms where data must be coded into 'chromosomes' (*see* section 5.2.2).

4.6.6 Data reduction

Apart from reducing the number of dimensions an important aspect is the reduction of data in terms of the actual records from the database that are used for discovery. There are two aspects to data reduction. First, the data source may be too large for the mining tools to be able to sift efficiently through the complete data set. Therefore, the data may need to be sampled. Secondly, the data set needs to be split into a training set and a test data set. The training data set is used for discovery purposes and model building while the test data set is used to assess the accuracy of the discovered knowledge on unseen data.

The most commonly used technique for unbiased sampling is random sampling. However, care needs to be taken when carrying out the sampling. It is important to make sure that the distribution of the data within the training set and test data set are as close as possible and representative of the real world being modelled. For example, in the case of the classification DMG, the distribution of the various classification labels should be similar in both data sets. In some cases, the data may be ordered by a particular attribute. In such situations a random sample may not contain a representative sample of the overall data set and care must be taken to ensure that the sample does so. For example, a housing database containing data on various houses in Northern Ireland, used for mass appraisal purposes, is sorted based on the ward that the house is in. The sample must be taken so that houses from each ward are represented in the sample and that the distribution of houses from each ward is similar to that in the overall data set. Such a biased sampling is called stratified sampling.

> **Step 7:** Pre-process the data by filling in missing values, enriching it through buying useful external data available, identifying and removing outliers, resolving heterogeneity, coding the data, as well as reducing its dimensionality and size

4.7 PATTERN DISCOVERY

The *pattern discovery* stage follows the data pre-processing stage. It consists of using algorithms that automatically discover patterns from the pre-processed data. The choice of algorithm depends on the discovery task at hand. Due to the large amounts of data from which knowledge is to be discovered, the algorithms used in this stage must be efficient.

Different methodologies require different parameters to be set by the user. While some methodologies have default parameter values through empirical investigations, others require these values to be set with caution as they can have a profound effect on the discovered knowledge. Example parameters are the number of hidden layers, the number of nodes per layer, the various learning parameters such as learning rate and error tolerance for neural networks, population size, mutation and cross-over probabilities for genetic algorithms, membership functions in fuzzy systems, support and confidence thresholds in association algorithms and so on.

Scalability of the pattern discovery algorithm is also an important issue (Small *et al.*, 1996). Scalability means that by taking advantage of parallel database management systems and additional CPUs the pattern recognition algorithms should be able to solve bigger problems as well as speed up the solutions without requiring major restructuring efforts.

Response times are as important in data mining as they are in OLTP queries. If the decision maker has to wait for hours before receiving the information requested he or she is certainly going to doubt the efficacy and usefulness of data mining as a decision support tool.

In our experience, it is better that the pattern discovery task is not totally automated and independent of user intervention. The domain expert can often provide domain knowledge that can be used by the discovery algorithm for making patterns in the data more visible, for pruning of the search space or for filtering the discovered knowledge based on a user-driven 'interestingness' measure.

This stage is often iterative, with knowledge discovered after each iteration leading to the refinement of the discovery goal (*see* section 4.10). The stage is the least human intensive of all the different stages of the data mining process as the mining algorithm used is normally automated.

In the manufacturing example the C4.5 tree induction algorithm was used for the classification DMG and exploratory data analysis for the deviation detection task.

> **Step 8:** Choose algorithm parameters carefully and discover regularities/patterns in the data

4.8   KNOWLEDGE POST-PROCESSING

The last stage of the data mining process is *knowledge post-processing*. This stage consists of two main parts: knowledge filtering and knowledge validation. We now discuss these two aspects in some detail and describe the most commonly used techniques to achieve them. This stage is carried out by the domain expert in conjunction with the data mining expert.

4.8.1 Knowledge filtering

Trivial and obsolete information must be filtered out and discovered knowledge must be presented in a user-readable way, using either visualisation techniques or natural language constructs. Often the knowledge filtering process is domain as well as user dependent. The need for knowledge filtering is more acute in some data mining tasks than others. One such task that requires good knowledge filtering techniques is the discovery of associations. As mentioned in section 5.1.1, one of the major problems with such discovery is that the number of patterns discoverable far exceeds the amount of data used for discovery. A common technique used for the filtering out of knowledge is to associate numeric values with the rules and defining thresholds on these values. The most commonly used values associated with association rules are *support* and *confidence* (also referred to as uncertainty). The support for a rule is the number of records in the database that satisfy the rule. Thus, if a rule has a support of 0.34, it means that the 34 per cent of the database from which the rule has been discovered satisfies the rule. The confidence in the rule is the belief that when the antecedent of the rule is true so is the consequent. Thus a confidence in a rule A $\longrightarrow$ B of 0.89 means that whenever a record in the database satisfies A, 89 per cent of such records also satisfy B. Sometimes a value called the 'interestingness' is also associated with a rule signifying how interesting the rule is. However, it is an accepted fact that a measure of rule interest is subjective and domain dependent, as well as dependent on the user and the problem at hand. Some generic concepts such as statistical independence and deviation from domain norms can be used to automate certain aspects of interestingness.

Another technique for knowledge filtering is the specifying of *syntactic constraints*. These constraints define attributes of interest as antecedents or consequents. For example, rules of interest to a domain expert in the retail industry may be rules that associate different products that result in milk products being bought or that are bought as a result of milk products being bought. Using such a constraint, only rules of the form below are interesting.

Meat and Eggs $\longrightarrow$ *Milk and Cream*
Curd $\longrightarrow$ *Beef and Peppers and Onions*

Thus, restricting the search space and the possible rules that may be discovered.

Another type of syntactic constraint is the *inter-attribute dependency constraint*. Attribute dependency constraints are of the type such that a rule containing *AccountAverageBalance* is interesting only if the account type is also part of the rule. Thus rules of the type

if Mortgage Customer = Yes
then AccountAverageBalance in [10K, 15K] and Occupation = Professional

are not interesting as the *AccountType* is not included in the rule whereas

if Mortgage Customer = Yes
then AccountAverageBalance in [10K, 15K] and AccountType =
Savings

is an interesting rule based simply on the inter-attribute dependency constraint specified. Note that based on threshold values for uncertainty, support or interestingness this rule may be filtered out.

An approach used by some data mining systems is to define what is interesting to the user and what is not. Interestingness is accepted as a subjective measure as what is interesting to one person may not be interesting to another. An interestingness measure takes into consideration the novelty of the knowledge, conspicuousness and deviation from the expected. Clearly, certain aspects of interestingness may be automated. For example, the measure of statistical independence and the χ^2 statistic are well-established measures of conspicuousness. Novelty deals with the concept of a discovery being interesting only if it cannot be deduced from knowledge previously discovered. Deviation from the expected is clearly subjective. What is expected depends on the user of the system. One technique suggested in literature is to build a user profile of the data based on what he or she knows about the data. Thus, only knowledge that deviates from the user profile of the data would be interesting. This is probably the most rewarding of the filtering techniques as recursively the system adapts to what the user finds interesting. Especially in domains that vary with time, knowledge discovered by the system and filtered manually may be incorporated into the user profile and used to filter out similar information discovered later.

For example, consider a scenario in the medical sector. The urology consultant knows safe ranges for different laboratory tests carried out for urology patients. He may set up these ranges to be the initial profile on his patient data so that whenever the laboratory results are downloaded onto his system from the laboratory database, he is only alerted whenever a laboratory result falls outside the test's safe range. A data mining system employed for clinical audit of urology patients discovers that most patients with uric acid levels outside the current safe range do not seem to develop any complications unless the levels are two standard deviations off the mean value. This information can then be incorporated into the profile and the consultant alerted only when the uric acid levels are outside the initial safe range by two standard deviations.

Data mining systems tend to use knowledge filtering measures in different ways. While some use these measures as a filter that only allows knowledge that satisfies pre-defined interestingness thresholds to be discovered, others utilise them to guide the search for new knowledge by incorporating them into the pattern discovery algorithm.

> **Step 9:** Filter out uninteresting and obvious patterns

4.8.2 Knowledge validation

The main aim of discovering knowledge is to be able to use it for decision support. Thus, it is important to ascertain what its accuracy will be on data other than the training data set. The simplest form of considering the classification DMT, accuracy measure is to split the data into two samples, one being the training set on which the knowledge is discovered and the test set on which the accuracy of the knowledge is tested. The overall accuracy is measured as the percentage of correctly classified examples in the test data. Such a measure does not, however, take into account the predictive accuracy of the knowledge for each individual class. The three most common techniques used for knowledge validation are discussed here.

Holdout or test sample estimation

In test sample estimation the data is partitioned into two mutually exclusive samples – one is used for training and the other (the holdout sample) is used for testing. The more examples in the test set the higher the bias of our estimate. However, with a smaller test set the confidence in the estimate will be lower. In *random subsampling*, the holdout method is repeated *n* times and the estimated accuracy is derived by averaging the runs.

Two points are worth noting about this technique of knowledge validation. First, the training and test data sets are not independent of each other: if a particular class is over-represented in the training set then it will be under-represented in the test data set as they are both part of the same data. Also, the holdout technique makes insufficient use of the data as it holds a part of the data out for testing purposes. Cross-validation solves these problems.

Cross-validation or rotation estimate

In *n*-fold cross-validation the data set is randomly partitioned into *n* subsets of approximately equal size. The inducer is trained on $n-1$ of these subsets and the other subset is used as a test data set. *n* such decision trees are induced each using a different subset as the test set. The cross-validation estimate of accuracy is the overall number of correct classifications divided by the total number of instances in the data set. In *stratified cross-validation*, the subsets are chosen such that the distribution of the different classes in each of the subsets reflects the distribution in the overall data set.

Cross-validation is a pessimistic estimate of the accuracy of the induced model and in practice the model performs better than the estimate provided by cross-validation. Most common variations of the cross-validation method used are ten-fold cross-validation and leave-one-out cross-validation. In ten-fold cross-validation, ten partitions of the data set are used and ten models induced. The average accuracy of these models is taken to be the expected accuracy of the model finally induced from the whole data set. In the leave-one-out variant, *n* models are induced, where *n* is the number of tuples in the data set. For each model induced, a single tuple is picked from the data set and set aside as the test data tuple. The average accuracy of the induced models is the expected accuracy of the final model induced from the whole data set.

Bootstrapping

Given a data set of *n* examples, a bootstrap sample is created by randomly picking *n* examples (with replacement) from the data set. The bootstrap sample created in this manner is used as the training set while the rest of the instances are used as the test data set. Bootstrapping is repeated *b* times and the average accuracy calculated from each bootstrap is taken to be the expected accuracy of a model discovered from the data.

> **Step 10:** Validate the interesting patterns

4.9   KNOWLEDGE MAINTENANCE

Due to the fact that the data used as input to the data mining process is often dynamic and prone to updates, the discovered knowledge has to be maintained. *Knowledge maintenance* may consist of reapplying the already set up data mining process for the particular problem or using an incremental methodology that would update the knowledge as the data changes keeping it consistent.

Taking into account the effort that has to be undertaken in order to rediscover the knowledge each time an update is made to the database, the preferred solution for updates to the database is to use incremental algorithms that can utilise information on the updates or changes made to the underlying data in the database and reflect these in the existing knowledge.

> **Step 11:** Set up a knowledge maintenance mechanism

4.10   REFINEMENT PROCESS

It is an accepted fact that the data mining process is iterative. After the knowledge post-processing stage, the knowledge discovered is examined by the domain expert and the data mining expert. This examination may lead to the *refinement process*, during which the domain knowledge as well as the actual goal of the discovery may be refined. Refinement of the goal of discovery could take the form of redefining the data used in the discovery, a change in the methodology used, the user defining additional constraints on the mining algorithm or refinement of the parameters of the mining algorithm. Once the refinement is complete the pattern discovery stage and the knowledge post-processing stages are repeated. Note that the refinement process is not a stage of the data mining process. Instead it constitutes the iterative aspects of the process and may make use of the initial stages, i.e. data prospecting, methodology identification, domain knowledge elicitation and data pre-processing. During the refinement process all three human experts play equally important roles.

Langley and Simon (1995) suggest that the main aim of machine learning is to improve the performance on some task. Data mining has precisely the same goal. Thus, once the knowledge has been discovered and verified, an important question to ask is: 'Are we actually better off now than we were before we started the data mining exercise?' If our objective is to improve our predictive accuracy in some domain, we need to check whether the accuracy of the discovered classifier actually outperforms the currently used technique. In situations where there is no current system in place, the induced classifier must improve on the baseline hypothesis. In the case of the classifier example, the baseline hypothesis would be 'all the examples are instances of the most common class in the training set'. For example, an induced classifier that classifies customers of an insurance company as likely to lapse or renew with an accuracy of 85 per cent may sound good at first. However, if 85 per cent of all customers renew their policies, assuming equal costs of misclassifying customers into the two classes the insurance company is no better off than assuming that all their customers renew their policy. In cases where the costs of misclassifying the customers are different for the different classes, a more complex measure would be required to calculate the monetary advantage incurred by the company by using the induced classifier.

> **Step 12:** Ask the question: 'Are we actually better off now than we were before we started the data mining exercise?'

5

Data mining goals
and methodologies

In this chapter we discuss in greater detail the taxonomy of data mining goals and methodologies at the disposal of the data miner. As discussed in Chapter 4, the methodology used is primarily dependent on the discovery goal at hand, which justifies the discussion of the discovery goals and methodologies together in this chapter.

5.1   DATA MINING GOALS

The data mining goals can be classified into eight main types:

- discovery of associations;

- classification;

- sequential pattern discovery;

- discovery of characteristics;

- clustering or data segmentation;

- deviation detection;

- regression; and

- temporal modelling.

While this taxonomy is complete taking into consideration work in the area reported in the literature, it is envisaged that as data mining matures further, new goals may be discovered and added. We now discuss these goals in greater detail.

5.1.1 Discovery of associations

The most publicised use of data mining in commercial settings is that of discovering associations within a supermarket. This application of data mining is often referred to as *basket analysis*. The aim of this type of discovery is to look for patterns in the data that associate one data element with another. For example, WalMart, a large retail chain in the US, discovered that on Fridays, a large percentage of people who buy nappies also buy a six-pack of beer. Such an association is so bizarre that it would be difficult to believe that any business domain expert would have thought of it. However, on further investigation (at the risk of sounding politically incorrect!) it was found that on Fridays on their way back from work men would stop at WalMart to pick up nappies, as directed by their wives, and being a Friday would get tempted to buy beer! Such an association if uncovered can result in the supermarkets changing their positioning of these items on their shelves to increase the sales of beer associated with nappy buyers.

An association rule is of the form $A \longrightarrow B$, where A and B are conjunctions of expressions on attributes of the database. A is referred to as the antecedent and B the consequent. Using this notation the WalMart example rule may be written as follows:

(Day = Friday) and (Product = Nappies) $\longrightarrow$ (Product = Beer)

The simple representation of such rules and their clear correspondence to natural language constructs make them very popular as examples of data mining success stories.

Though basket analysis is the typical example used for the discovery of associations, it is not the only use. In fact, associations are the most basic type of pattern. They are the purest form of data mining and include classification (*see* section 5.1.2) and characteristic (*see* section 5.1.4) rules as special cases. The definition of an association is so loose that it is difficult at times to justify such patterns as knowledge rather than as just a summary of the data. The number of discoverable association patterns far exceed the amount of data being used to discover them. The discovery of such associations is useful only in conjunction with user guidance in the form of parameter setting for filtering out obvious and non-interesting associations. The most commonly used parameters are threshold values for the support of and confidence in (or uncertainty of) a rule. Support is the ratio of the number of the records in the database for which the rule is true to the total number of records in the database. Confidence in a rule is the belief in the consequent being true for a record once the antecedent is known to be true. Figure 5.1 illustrates these measures. Section 4.8 discusses filtering of association rules in greater detail.

Figure 5.1
SUPPORT AND CONFIDENCE

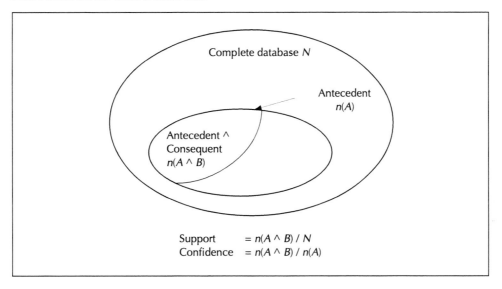

Complete database N

Antecedent
$n(A)$

Antecedent ∧
Consequent
$n(A ∧ B)$

Support   = $n(A ∧ B) / N$
Confidence = $n(A ∧ B) / n(A)$

Table 5.1
SAMPLE OF AN EMPLOYMENT DATABASE

Customer#	Age	Income £	Car_Type	Occupation	Dependants
10011	45	100 010	Family	Manager	0
10012	54	100 100	Family	Professor	2
10013	33	113 000	Sports	Salesman	0
10014	32	12 000	None	Shop assistant	0
10015	21	24 000	Jeep	Archaeologist	1
10016	45	2 000	None	P/T cleaner	3
10017	80	242 000	Sports	Director	1

Consider the sample from an employment database shown in Table 5.1. According to the definition of associations, each record in the table could be the source of a number of association rules. Thus, from this sample of seven records and six attributes the number of associations that can be discovered is immense if no support and uncertainty thresholds are set. Table 5.2 shows some of the associations that can be discovered from the first record of the sample database.

Table 5.2
SAMPLE RULES FROM EMPLOYEE DATABASE

Age = 45 and Income = 100 010
       $\longrightarrow$ Car_Type = Family (support = $\frac{1}{7}$, confidence = 1)

Age = 45
       $\longrightarrow$ Income = 100 010 and Car_Type = Family (support = $\frac{1}{7}$,
           confidence = $\frac{1}{2}$)

Customer# = 10011 and Age = 45
       $\longrightarrow$ Income = 100 010 and Car_Type = Family and Occupation =
           Manager and Dependants = 0 (support = $\frac{1}{7}$, confidence = 1)

Customer# = 10011 and Age = 45 and Income = 100 010
       $\longrightarrow$ Car_Type = Family and Occupation = Manager and
           Dependants = 0 (support = $\frac{1}{7}$, confidence = 1)

Customer# = 10011
       $\longrightarrow$ Age = 45 (support = $\frac{1}{7}$, confidence = 1)

Age = 45
       $\longrightarrow$ Customer# = 10011 (support = $\frac{1}{7}$, confidence = $\frac{1}{2}$)

(And so on)

From the example rules in Table 5.2 it is clear that discovery of associations that involve unique attributes, for example *Customer#*, is fruitless as their applicability is minimal. Such attributes need to be discarded before association rules are discovered. Also thresholds on the support and confidence are a minimal requirement for sensible discovery. In Appendix 1 it is shown how association rule discovery algorithms can be applied to discover useful knowledge.

5.1.2 Classification

Learning classification rules from data is probably the most thoroughly studied field in machine learning. Machine learning researchers argue that this restriction to classification is not as severe as it may sound as most complex processes can be decomposed into a series of classification problems.

Classification rules are rules that discriminate between different partitions of a database based on their attributes. The partitions of the database are based on an attribute called the classification label. Each value within the classification label domain is called a class. Consider the sample data from a car insurance company shown in Table 5.3. The field *LapseRenew* partitions the database into two classes: customers who have allowed their insurance policy to lapse (*LapseCustomers*) and customers who have renewed their insurance policy (*RenewCustomers*). The insurance company would clearly benefit from being able to predict in advance whether a customer was going to allow their policy to relapse or renew it as they could pursue customers at a high risk of the former to try and change their mind. Classification rules can be discovered to discriminate between *LapseCustomers* and *RenewCustomers*. From the sample data in Table 5.2, a simple classification rule would be:

if Age < 30 then Lapse else Renew

or

if No Claims [0,1] then Lapse else Renew

Table 5.3
SAMPLE DATA FROM INSURANCE COMPANY

Cust. No.	Insurance group	Age of car	Age of driver	No claims	LapseRenew
10011	4	10	21	0	Lapse
10012	5	7	24	1	Lapse
10013	8	3	26	1	Lapse
00212	2	16	56	8	Renew
00131	9	2	62	10	Renew

In real-world problems, however, classification rules are more complex as the search space of most real-world processes is more complex than that shown in the examples above. Also, for any data set there are a number of possible classification rules. Thus, the objective of classification algorithms is to discover the best set of classification rules in terms of simplicity, information content and accuracy.

It is important to note at this stage that classification algorithms require both, positive as well as negative examples of the concept that they are trying to learn. Thus, to learn to identify customer lapse and renewal it is necessary to supply the algorithm with data pertaining to customers belonging to both classes. The positive and negative examples together constitute the training data set and the customers that need to be classified into potentially lapse and potentially renew customers are called the test data set. Classification rules discovered are the sufficient conditions for a record to belong to a class, i.e. knowing that the customer has the attributes in the antecedent of a rule for a class implies that the customer will belong to that class.

Also worth noting is the relationship between classification and association rules. As mentioned in section 5.1.1, classification rules are a special case of associations. In classification rules the consequent is fixed to the classification label and only those premises appear in the antecedent that are sufficient conditions for the membership of the class. This is a form of syntactic constraint defined in section 4.8.1.

5.1.3 Sequential pattern discovery

Sequential pattern discovery is similar to discovery of associations. The difference here is that sequential pattern discovery techniques discover associations across time. For example, consider the sample database in Table 5.4. A sequential pattern may be that whenever somebody buys a jacket and a tie, the next time they shop they buy a pair of shoes. Knowing such information could result in the store attempting to get the customer to buy the pair of shoes in the same transaction by placing the shoes section close to the jacket section as it is possible that the customer may purchase the shoes at a competitor's store instead.

Table 5.4
EXAMPLE RETAIL TRANSACTION DATABASE

Cust. No.	Date/Time		Jacket	Tie	Shoes	Socks	Shirt
1001	02.06.96	09:25	1	1	0	0	0
1002	02.06.96	10:32	1	1	0	1	0
1001	03.06.96	13:34	0	0	1	0	0
1003	04.06.96	13:30	1	0	0	0	0
1003	06.06.96	10:02	0	0	1	0	1
1002	06.06.96	12:03	0	0	1	0	1

A sequential pattern is in the form $(A)_{t_i} \longrightarrow (B)_{t_j}$, where A and B are conjunctions of expressions on attributes of the database and the attributes in A appear in the database with an earlier time stamp than B, i.e. $t_i < t_j$. Using this notation the example rule above may be written as follows:

Jacket and Tie $\longrightarrow$ Shoes with support = $^2/_3$ and confidence = 1

Sequential patterns, like association rules, have a defined support and confidence value. Also, support and confidence threshold values and other filtering techniques applicable to association rules are applicable to sequential patterns as well.

5.1.4 Discovery of characteristics

A characteristic rule is an assertion that characterises a concept. For example, the symptoms of a disease are characteristics of that disease. A characteristic rule is a kind of association rule where the antecedent is constrained as the concept being characterised. As such they are the best type of characterisation of a concept that can be arrived at in the absence of negative examples. They constitute the necessary condition for a concept as opposed to a sufficient condition represented by classification rules. Thus, they can be considered as a less accurate form of classification rules that are arrived at in the absence of negative examples. Characteristic rules may be refined as negative examples are collected and may incrementally be converted into classification rules.

Table 5.5
EXAMPLE DATA SET FROM A BANK

Cust. No.	Income	Post Code	Age	Dependants	Product
10011	42 000	BT10	52	1	Savings
10012	50 000	BT7	24	8	Current
10013	80 000	BT3	56	1	Mortgage
00212	22 000	BT16	58	1	Mortgage
00131	19 000	BT2	62	10	Current

Consider the example customer database of a bank in Table 5.5. Now suppose the bank wants to utilise its customer base to the fullest, by cross-selling its products to existing customers (*see* Appendix 1). The data seems very similar to that in Table 5.3; however, there is one very important difference, based on the goal of discovery. The field *Product* in the database consists of separate classes but the nature of cross-selling will not allow the use of a classification approach, as detailed in section 5.1.2. For example, if the bank wants to sell mortgage products to existing customers, it cannot use data on customers other than mortgage customers as negative examples. Remember that classification rules differentiate between positive and negative examples. As non-mortgage customers are also the target set, differentiating between them and mortgage customers will not provide useful cross-sales rules. In order to use the classification approach, data would be required on customers who have refused a mortgage product with the bank. Such data is not normally stored in the bank's database. Thus, in such a situation characteristic rules need to be discovered for mortgage customers and these used for cross-sales.

In general, characteristic rules are of the form:

Class Label = C ⟶ *A$_1$ = a$_{1_i}$ and ... and A$_s$ = a$_{s_i}$*

where *A$_i$*s are attributes and *C* is a particular class. For example:

Product = Mortgage ⟶ *Dependants = 1 and Age in [50, 59]*

This rule would imply that customer 10011 is a potential customer for a mortgage.

If, instead, we were using a classification algorithm we would get a rule similar to the following:

if Dependants = 1

    if Age in [56, 58] ⟶ *Product = Mortgage*

else

    if Age in [30, 40] ⟶ *Product = Savings*

Using this rule, customer 10011 will be classified as a savings customer and not as a potential mortgage customer.

The classification rules can be used to suggest the most appropriate product to new customers. However, they cannot be used to target existing customers as can characteristic rules. Figure 5.2 shows the difference between the goals of classification and characteristic rule discovery. While savings and current account customers are viewed as negative examples of the concept mortgage customer by the classification discovery algorithm, they are viewed as the target set by the characteristic rule discovery algorithm, both views being appropriate views based on the goal of the discovery. It is worth noting that the non-mortgage customers being 'binned' are the true negative examples in the case of characteristic rule discovery and are not identifiable within the customer database in the first place. If these customers were identifiable, a classification approach would have been appropriate for use in cross-sales.

Figure 5.2
CLASSIFICATION VS CHARACTERISTIC RULE DISCOVERY

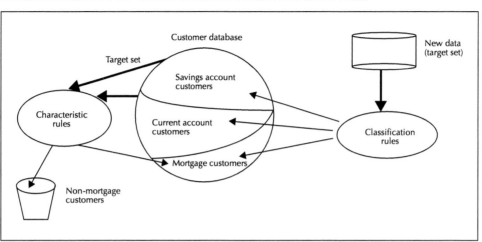

Normal measures associated with these rules are support, confidence and interestingness. While support and confidence have the same interpretation as in the case of association rules, the interestingness measure that seems most suitable is the deviation of the customer characteristics in the consequent of the rule from the general characteristics in the customer base (*see* Appendix 1).

5.1.5 Clustering or data segmentation

Cluster analysis or data segmentation, often referred to in machine learning literature as *unsupervised learning*, deals with the discovery of structure in data. Cluster analysis differs from classification in that the classes to which the data tuples in the training set belong are not provided. The inductive learning algorithm has to identify the classes by finding similarities between different states provided as examples. This process is called *learning by observation and discovery*. Initial clustering techniques were based on the Euclidean distance between the data tuples, and algorithms developed for clustering attempted to maximise the similarity within a class while minimising the similarity among the different classes. However, these systems could deal only with numeric data and were unable to use background information. Conceptual clustering attempts to overcome the drawbacks of traditional clustering techniques by employing not only the Euclidean distance measures for numeric values but also by employing the hierarchical concept generalisations made available by domain experts to deal with non-numeric attributes within the data. Clusters may or may not be exclusive, i.e. one data record in the database may fall into more than one cluster.

An investigation of these clusters, possibly using classification algorithms, could lead to discovery of distinguishing characteristics of the different clusters. Note that clustering can be viewed as a first step in the discovery process and is not normally an end in itself.

The easiest way to view clusters within multi-dimensional data is to consider an imaginary mapping of this data into two dimensions and forming groups within the plane of projection. Figure 5.3 shows clusters in a two-dimensional space.

Figure 5.3
A SIMPLE TWO-DIMENSIONAL CLUSTERING

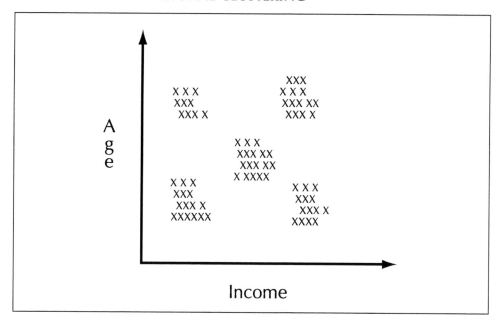

5.1.6 Deviation detection

A deviation is defined as the difference between an observed value and a reference value. For example, a company that normally spends £10 000 per month on employee perks would be interested in discovering months where the amount spent is over £15 000. It would also be interested in locating the reasons behind this deviation. Detection of deviations and explaining them is the data mining goal of deviation detection.

Deviations are of a number of types: deviation over time, normative deviation and deviation from expectation. These three types of deviation differ in the norm used to calculate the deviation of the observed value. In deviation over time, the norm would be based on the value of the variable over a certain time period in the past. For example, last year's third quarter could be the norm against which this year's third quarter value is compared. When a standard norm is available as a reference, deviation from that value is referred to as normative deviation. In deviation from expectation, the expected value may be generated from a model or may be based on a hypothesis provided by a domain expert.

A discovery system based on deviation detection consists of a number of components. First, a component for identifying significant deviations from user defined norms is required. Next, a component is required that can order the deviations in terms of the most interesting and can remove any redundant results. Next, the deviations must be explained. An explanation may come from a decomposition of a formula that defines the finding measured. For example:

TotalPerks = ChildEducation * NumberOfChildren + Sales * 0.1.

It may turn out that the number of children eligible for the company's children's education scheme far exceeded the norm. Thus, the more interesting deviation is the number of children of the company's employees eligible for the children's education scheme as opposed to the deviation in the *TotalPerks* payment made by the company.

Alternatively, the explanation may be arrived at by breaking down the measure into values from subsectors formed by decomposing the sector of the finding. For example, if the sales of a particular whisky brand are found to be very high in Scotland in 1996, the reason may be that the product had greater sales only in Edinburgh during the summer, whereas in the rest of Scotland the sales have been normal. This in turn could be explained by a larger number of tourists visiting Edinburgh during that period due to a new advertising policy of the Scottish Tourist Board.

The final component of the discovery system is the report generator, including possible recommendations for rectifying the deviations discovered.

Deviation detection has proved useful in certain sectors where there are set measures for performance and deviations from these norms are of interest. For example, KEFIR (Key Findings Reporter), a domain-independent system for discovering and explaining key findings based on deviation detection, was very successful in the healthcare sector because predefined measures for deviation detection such as *AverageHospitalPaymentsPerCapita* and *AdmissionRatePer1000* are available in this domain. In this respect, KEFIR is user-driven and discovery is performed in predefined paths. However, deviation detection can be automated as well and is the basis of belief system-based interestingness measures for knowledge discovered using techniques other than deviation detection. This data mining task closely resembles the goal of OLAP though semi-automated deviation detection could be used to navigate through the multi-dimensional hypercube of data stored in an OLAP engine, highlighting the interesting areas for human evaluation.

5.1.7 Regression

Regression is the learning of a function that maps attributes onto a real-valued domain. Regression can be thought of as classification, the only difference being that the classification label, instead of being discrete, is continuous (*see* section 3.2). An example would be the process of house price prediction. The attribute that is being predicted is called a *dependent variable* while the attributes that are used to predict the dependent variable are referred to as *independent variables.*

Consider the example data set from a real estate database shown in Table 5.6. Here the price attribute is the dependent variable and the objective of the regression is to discover a model that would predict the price of the house based on the other attributes. The independent variables may be numeric or qualitative in nature. As in the case of classification, the rules discovered in the case of regression can also be used to predict the price for houses other than those in the training data set.

Table 5.6
SAMPLE FROM HOUSING DATABASE

Ward	House Type	Heating	Bedrooms	Garage	Price
1	Bungalow	Oil-fired	4	Double	130 500
1	Bungalow	Oil-fired	3	Single	110 750
1	Terraced	None	2	None	43 000
2	Terraced	Economy 7	2	None	44 000
2	House	Gas-fired	6	Single	140 000
3	House	Gas-fired	8	Single	150 000

5.1.8 Temporal modelling

This data mining goal involves rules that are based on temporal data. Suppose we have a database of natural disasters. If we conclude from such a database that whenever there was an earthquake in Los Angeles the next day Mt Kilimanjaro erupted, such a rule would be a temporal pattern. Such rules are useful for making predictions which could be used in making market gains or for taking preventive action against natural disasters.

From a business perspective, the most well-known applications of temporal modelling are in financial forecasting. For example, consider the stock prices data shown in Fig. 5.4. Conclusions drawn from such data like 'whenever the price of Microsoft shares falls for two days in succession, IBM shares rise by around 2 per cent' or 'Microsoft share prices never fall for more than three successive days' can be useful to financial investors. Like sequential patterns, temporal patterns may have support and confidence measures associated with them.

Figure 5.4
SHARE PRICE DATA

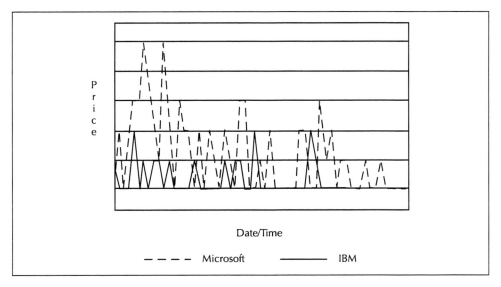

5.2   DATA MINING METHODOLOGIES

Data mining methodologies may be classified into five main types based on their origin. These are:

• traditional statistics;

• machine learning techniques;

• uncertainty-based techniques;

• database techniques; and

• visualisation.

However, most data mining solutions in the real world rely on more than one methodology and are in that respect hybrid methodologies.

5.2.1 Traditional statistics

Statistical techniques may be employed for data mining at a number of stages of the mining process. Such techniques have been employed traditionally by analysts to detect and explain unusual patterns. However, using statistical techniques and interpreting their results is difficult and requires a considerable amount of knowledge of statistics. Data mining seeks to provide non-statisticians with useful information that is not difficult to interpret. We now discuss how statistical techniques can be used within data mining.

Data cleansing

The presence of data which is erroneous or irrelevant (outliers) may impede the mining process. While such data therefore needs to be distinguished, this task is particularly sensitive, as some outliers may be of considerable interest in providing the knowledge that mining seeks to find: 'good' outliers need to be retained for further investigation separate from the main discovery process, while 'bad' outliers should be removed. Bad outliers may arise from sources such as human or mechanical errors in experimental measurement, from the failure to convert measurements to a consistent scale, or from slippage in time-series measurements. Good outliers are those outliers that may be characteristic of the real-world scenario being modelled. While these are often of particular interest to users, knowledge about them may be difficult to come by and is frequently more critical than knowledge about more commonly occurring situations. The presence of outliers may be detected by methods involving thresholding the difference between particular attribute values and the average, using either parametric or non-parametric methods.

Exploratory data analysis

Exploratory data analysis concentrates on simple arithmetic and easy-to-draw pictures to provide *descriptive statistical measures and presentation*, such as frequency counts and table construction (including frequencies, row, column and total percentages), building histograms, computing measures of location (mean, median), spread (standard deviation, range, as well as quartiles and semi inter-quartile range).

Data selection

In order to improve the efficiency and increase the time performance of data analysis, it is necessary to provide sampling facilities to reduce the scale of computation. Sampling is an efficient way of discovering knowledge and re-sampling offers opportunities for cross-validation. Hierarchical data structures may be explored by segmentation and stratification.

Attribute re-definition

We may define new variables which are more meaningful than the previous, e.g. BodyMassIndex = Weight/Height^2. Alternatively we may want to change the granularity of the data, e.g. age in years may be grouped into ages 0–20 years, 20–40 years, 40–60 years, 60+ years. Principal component analysis (PCA) is of particular interest to data mining as most data mining algorithms have linear time complexity with respect to the number of tuples in the database, but are exponential with respect to the number of attributes in the data. Attribute reduction using PCA therefore provides a facility to account for a large proportion of the variability of the original attributes by considering only relatively few new attributes (called principal components) which are specially constructed as weighted linear combinations of the original attributes. The first principal component is that weighted linear combination of attributes with the maximum variation; the second principal component is that weighted linear combination which is orthogonal to the first while maximising the variation, etc. The new attributes formed by PCA may possibly themselves be assigned individual meaning if domain knowledge is invoked, or they may be used as inputs to further data mining. The facility for PCA requires the partial computation of the eigensystem of the correlation matrix, as the principal component weights are the eigenvector components with the eigenvalues giving the proportions of the variance explained by each principal component.

Data analysis

Statistics provides a number of tools for data analysis some of which may be employed within data mining. These include:

- *measures of association and relationships between attributes,* such as computation of expected frequencies and construction of cross-tabulations, computation of chi-squared statistics of association, presentation of scatterplots and computation of correlation coefficients. The interestingness of rules may be assessed by considering measures of statistical significance (Piatetski-Shapiro, 1991);

- *inferential statistics* for hypothesis testing, such as construction of confidence intervals, parametric and non-parametric hypothesis tests for average values and for group comparisons;

- *classification* may be carried out using discriminant analysis (supervised) or cluster analysis (unsupervised).

Machine learning techniques

Machine learning researchers tend to identify themselves with one of five main paradigms of machine learning (Langley and Simon, 1995). These are:

- rule induction;

- genetic algorithms;

- neural networks;

- instance-based or case-based reasoning; and

- analytic learning.

Of these, the first four paradigms have been applied to data mining with varying degrees of success. Langley and Simon (1995) suggest that the distinctions made between these paradigms are more from a historical rather than a scientific viewpoint. While all these paradigms aim to achieve the same goal of improved performance in solving a task by exploiting regularities in data, they differ in the metaphors used. For example, while proponents of neural networks emphasise analogies with neuroscience, proponents of genetic algorithms draw parallels with evolution, case-based reasoning with human memory and rule induction with heuristic search. However, these differences are now less pronounced and hybrid systems that utilise more than one of these paradigms together are becoming commonplace, for example neuro-fuzzy and neuro-genetic algorithms. In this section we briefly describe these paradigms.

Rule induction

The dictionary definition of induction is 'a process of reasoning by which a general conclusion is drawn from a set of premises, based mainly on experience and experimental evidence'. Thus, the basic idea of rule induction is to build a model of the environment using sets of data describing the environment. The simplest model clearly is to store all the states of the environment along with all the transitions between them over time. For example, a chess game may be modelled by storing each state of the chess board along with the transitions from one state to the other. But the usefulness of such a model is limited as the number of states and transitions between them are infinite in many real-world applications. Thus, it is unlikely that a state that occurs in the future would match, exactly, a state from the past. Thus, a better model would be to store abstractions/generalisations of the states and the associated transitions. The process of generalisation from data (specific instantiations of the real-world process) is called *induction*.

Genetic algorithms

Genetic algorithms (Srinivas and Patnaik, 1994) were first proposed by John Holland in the early 1970s but have gained momentum only in the last decade. They model the evolutionary process and are based on the principle of survival of the fittest. Genetic algorithms start with a population of solutions represented as binary strings that are the equivalent of a gene pool in nature. Each string has an associated fitness value that directly influences its chances of surviving in the next population. The selected candidate strings are subjected to crossover and mutation (regeneration of lost genetic material) – two genetic operations that take place in nature. The crossed and mutated strings form the new population and the whole process is repeated until a certain stopping criterion is arrived at. Thus, genetic algorithms iteratively search the search space in parallel arriving at the global optima, i.e. the best model of the data at convergence.

Neural networks

Neural networks, also known as artificial neural networks to differentiate them from biological neural networks, find their inspiration from neuroscience. The realisation that most symbolic learning paradigms are not satisfactory in a number of domains, e.g. pattern recognition, which are regarded by humans as trivial led to research into trying to model the human brain. In reality, an artificial neural network is very different from a biological neural network but does have a number of commonalties as well. An artificial neurone or processing element is a highly simplified model of the biological neurone. As in biological neurones an artificial neurone has a number of inputs, a body and an output which can be connected to a number of other artificial neurones. Neural networks are densely interconnected networks of processing elements together with a rule to adjust the strength of the connections between the units in response to externally supplied data, normally referred to as a training data set. The overall behaviour of a network is determined by its connectivity rather than by the detailed operation of any element. The learning algorithms used are normally iterative, e.g. the back-propagation algorithm iteratively attempts to reduce the error in the output of the network. Once the error is reduced the network can be used to classify other unseen objects.

Neural networks can be used in data mining for classification, regression as well as clustering (Bigus, 1996). One of the major problems with using neural networks is that they are 'black-boxes'. As the knowledge is stored in the neural network in the form of the connection strengths between different processing elements, the knowledge is unintelligible. Thus, neural networks are more useful in domains like critical process control where understanding the knowledge is not as necessary as the accuracy of the prediction.

Case-based reasoning

Case-based reasoning (CBR) is a machine learning paradigm modelled on the human problem-solving process. When a new problem is encountered, the problem-solving process followed by humans is to remember a previous problem that is similar to the present problem, adapt it based on the difference between it and the present problem, and then apply the new, adapted solution.

A CBR system consists of a case base containing previous problems and their solutions, a similarity measure that is used as a measure of how similar two cases are, an indexing mechanism accessing similar cases, a set of adaptation rules used to adapt the retrieved case to solve the present problem, and domain knowledge that may be used in defining the similarity measure.

Normally case bases incorporate a certain amount of domain knowledge and structuring that transform databases into case bases. However, in their simplest form, a case base could be a database. Thus, using this simplistic model of a CBR system, CBR has been used for data mining tasks with classification or regression goals. Also algorithms like nearest neighbour used by CBR systems for retrieval of similar cases have been used for classification and clustering data mining goals. However, one of the major drawbacks of using CBR systems is the initial set-up costs associated with it, i.e. acquiring the adaptation knowledge. This bottleneck is reminiscent of the bottleneck associated with building rule-based systems. However, CBR has great potential for use in conjunction with other data mining paradigms providing goal-oriented mining. A discussion on this subject is, however, outside the realms of this book.

In conclusion, CBR is a successful paradigm of machine learning and has great potential in data mining. However, given the present difficulties with its use in data mining, it has had limited success. Areas where CBR can be utilised are where domain expertise is available to provide the required adaptation knowledge. Other paradigms of machine learning related to CBR are instance-based learning and learning by analogy.

Uncertainty-based techniques

Uncertainty modelling has been an important issue in knowledge-based systems since their inception. Modelling uncertainty is difficult due to the different sources of uncertainty (e.g. noise, lack of confidence, unreliability and ignorance) as well as its different aspects (e.g. imprecision, vagueness and ambiguity).

A number of alternative approaches to modelling uncertainty have been suggested in artificial intelligence literature. Of these, the most commonly used in data mining are Bayesian belief networks, fuzzy set theory and, more recently, rough set theory.

Bayesian belief networks

Initial knowledge-based systems utilised probability theory as the uncertainty model, though it soon became apparent that alternative techniques would be required. This was mainly due to two reasons. First, the representation used by probability theory was found to be too restrictive, and second, probabilistic techniques available at the time required many parameters to be defined by the user or assumed unrealistic sets of independence relationships (Heckerman *et al.*, 1995). Bayesian belief networks (BBNs) aim to remove these restrictions.

A BBN is a graphical technique that is used to model uncertain information within an environment based on relationships between variables of the environment. Though the arcs represent dependencies between variables within the problem domain, they can be interpreted as cause–effect relationships or influence relationships. Thus, BBNs are also known as cause–effect networks and influence diagrams. Figure 5.5 shows an example BBN for car engine troubleshooting (Heckerman *et al.*, 1995). The interpretation of the independence relationships as cause–effect relationships makes BBNs an intuitive mode of communication between experts and knowledge engineers and has been a major reason for their success in recent expert system development.

Figure 5.5
EXAMPLE OF A BAYESIAN BELIEF NETWORK

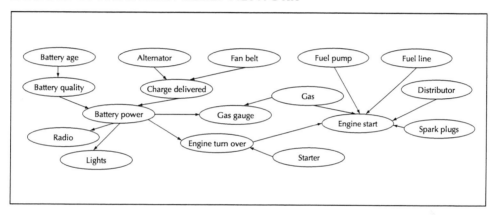

These networks are underpinned by well established Bayesian probability techniques allowing probabilistic information to be inferred from them. The discovery of these models from data is, however, still in its infancy reducing their utility in data mining. However, a number of real-world applications employing such models within knowledge-based systems using knowledge engineering techniques have been reported (Heckerman *et al.*, 1995).

Fuzzy set theory

Fuzzy set theory has been most successful in control applications and a number of such applications have been reported in the real world, especially in Japan. However, techniques developed for fuzzy data analysis such as fuzzy clustering, linguistic summaries using fuzzy techniques and fuzzy rule discovery can be used for data mining.

Rough set theory

Rough set theory is a new technique for dealing with uncertain information. A major advantage of rough set theory with respect to data mining is that, unlike other techniques that require certain parameters, e.g. probability distributions in Bayesian techniques and membership functions in fuzzy set theory, it utilises only the information that can be derived from the data itself.

Rough set theory is a powerful tool for reducing the dimensionality of the data and discovering data dependencies. Thus it can be used in conjunction with other data mining methodologies to discover various kinds of knowledge addressing various data mining goals. Rough set theory is now accepted as a mainstream data mining methodology.

5.2.4 Database techniques

Attribute-oriented induction and set-oriented approaches to data mining attempt to employ facilities provided by present DBMSs to discover knowledge. This allows the use of years of research into database performance enhancement to be used within data mining processes. However, SQL is very limited in what it can provide for data mining and therefore techniques based solely on this approach are very limited in applicability.

Typical facilities of the DBMS utilised by these data mining methodologies are indexes and query optimisation. Extensions have been suggested to standard SQL to incorporate discovery tasks, with the ultimate goal of creating a data mining management system that encompasses present DBMSs.

5.2.5 Visualisation

'A picture can say more than a thousand words' is the basic principle behind the use of visualisation as a data mining tool. Data and knowledge visualisation can enhance the interface between the user and the data mining system and in some cases is enough to discover the required patterns.

Visualisation techniques are most useful in exploratory data analysis and knowledge visualisation. Knowledge visualisation techniques depend on the type of knowledge discovered. Most data mining software incorporates visualisation techniques ranging from simple interactive graphs like histograms, distributions and scatterplots to more futuristic virtual reality type visualisation of knowledge discovered by the data mining algorithms. More advanced techniques are visualising knowledge in more than two dimensions and the provision of navigation or fly-through capabilities, e.g. for decision trees.

5.2.6 Hybrid techniques

Hybrid techniques use a mixture of the best features of each of the data mining methodologies. For example, neural networks have been used in conjunction with genetic algorithms. Genetic algorithms are robust search algorithms that discover the optimal solution to a problem avoiding local minima. During the training of a neural network, the idea is to find the optimal weights that maximise the neural network's predictive accuracy. Thus, genetic algorithms can be used to discover these optimal weights. Other examples of hybrid systems are neuro-fuzzy systems, fuzzy case-based reasoning systems and genetic/nearest neighbour systems.

6

The data mining strategy

Many IT-led data mining projects do not succeed because trivial facts are not considered, technology is applied incorrectly or users are not involved appropriately. Introducing data mining to an enterprise, no matter on what level and to what extent, is a challenging task which requires strategic expertise to avoid commonly made mistakes and to minimise risks and costs as much as possible. In this chapter, first, common mistakes, risks and costs are described and methods to avoid them are outlined. Second, a taxonomy of points to bear in mind when setting up a data mining environment is given, and finally, scenarios are described to show how a business can be reengineered to facilitate data mining.

6.1   COMMON MISTAKES, RISKS AND COSTS

In this section strategic – not technical – principles in the introduction of data mining to an enterprise are shown.

6.1.1 Common mistakes and risks

Data mining is a decision support technology, it is not the omnipotent panacea which achieves miracles. Recently, data mining capabilities have frequently been overestimated, and wrong expectations have led to predictable disappointments which could be quite expensive to overcome.

Note that data mining is meant to be a decision *support* tool – it does not take any responsibilities away from decision making which still has to be performed by a human user. It merely provides the decision maker with knowledge. It is up to the decision makers to use their wisdom in applying the knowledge optimally.

A corporation has a number of departments with varying business requirements, and so no one single tool can solve all problems. Existing data mining tools are very powerful in specific areas (*see* Appendix 2), but off-the-shelf tools themselves carry two generic risks. First, they have to be applied appropriately, and second, the functionality a specific tool provides might not solve the problems at hand. It is very important to gauge what kind of information is required by the corporate decision makers and tools appropriate for the particular requirement need to be chosen. Data mining may be regarded as a service rather than as just an off-the-shelf tool. Most successful data mining projects have been instances where the tool chosen is specific to the market sector, e.g. AT&T's sales and marketing packs in telecommunication and GTEs Health-KEFIR in healthcare.

When introducing data mining, various goals have to be formulated carefully, and project and corporation objectives kept in mind. Short-term goals include the discovery of required knowledge for a particular problem, or analysis of existing data for a short-term decision. Mid-term goals contain the achievement of results which influence decision making in the near future, whereas long-term goals consider data mining as one of the key factors for decision making about the long-term strategy of the business.

Data mining must be user-led, which requires the allocation of appropriate human resources in the appropriate position at the appropriate time. Assuming that a data expert or domain specialist can easily take on data mining expertise will end in the misuse of data mining techniques and lead to disappointing or useless results. Also, as mentioned earlier, it is very important that the human resources (data expert, domain expert, and data mining expert) are brought together early on in the process, as any project that does not bring together this expertise right at the beginning will very likely encounter problems later on. It is also essential to identify groups of knowledge workers and decision makers who will apply the results.

6.1.2 Hidden costs of data mining

Effect on production systems

Production systems have been built with the collection and manipulation of data in mind. Their design is based around making specific OLTP queries efficient. When using data for decision support the requirements from the system are different. Data required needs to be collated from different database tables using table joins. Such joins create a large overhead on the production system especially when they are distributed over more than 5–10 tables, which are commonplace in decision support queries. The OLTP type queries are therefore bound to suffer. Thus, in situations where the OLTP queries are crucial, data mining exercises should be performed on secondary data stores, e.g. data warehouses or 'backup' databases, where possible.

Data extraction costs

In situations in which a data warehouse or secondary data store does not exist, data must be downloaded from the production system into flat ASCII files and data mining performed on a platform separate from those used by OLTP applications. This extraction of data is not normally straightforward either and, depending on the data mining tool to be used, it may require some data transformation as well. Additional resources for this purpose must be taken into account when costing a data mining solution.

Resistance to change – 'the law of inertia'

The introduction of IT solutions within an organisation requires a whole new work ethic. IT affects employees at all levels of the organisation. Therefore, the introduction of IT is often met with resistance. We have already pointed out, in section 4.3, how employees need to be made aware at the data acquisition stage of the process of the benefits of the system. At the knowledge utilisation stage similar awareness exercises are necessary for the system to be successful as well as worthwhile. *The Financial Times* reported on 28 November 1995 in an article on data mining that 'marketing experts are often torn between admiration for analytical power that these technologies [data mining] provide, and regret as it is displacing creativity, intuition and judgement.' However, this seems unjust as data mining only provides the decision maker with information that is needed to make the decision – whatever decision is reached by using this information is still in the hands of decision maker. Thus, data mining provides the marketing experts with the information that they require to make better decisions – it does not hamper the decision process in any way.

6.2   SETTING UP A DATA MINING ENVIRONMENT

In addition to the personnel, organisational as well as strategic requirements and limitations described above, a battery of technical equipment is required to perform data mining appropriately. These facilities are used in one or more steps of the data mining process, as described in Chapter 4.

One obvious but often underestimated issue is the accessibility of data that has to be sought. Sometimes data is not available because of security or confidentiality reasons. In an IT landscape with different network topologies, operating systems and database management systems, accessibility can be very problematic. Furthermore, data might be incompatible with each other, which means that a facility to solve such heterogeneity is required.

An ideal platform for such data is a data warehouse because it provides multi-database access. Additionally, different subject-oriented views of the data are represented, which allow problem-specific data mining. A data warehouse is semi-static, i.e. it is not only updated on-line, and stores historic data. Both facts help in the performance of data mining accordingly. Data warehouses often provide facilities for data cleansing, but sometimes special tools are required, again dependent on the task at hand. It must be borne in mind that introducing a data warehouse is a long-term investment and should not only focus on the data mining aspects, but also consider enterprise-wide infrastructural strategies.

Data mining is often applied to quite complex data sets, which causes two difficulties. First is the storage space which is needed for the data and the discovered knowledge, and second is resulting poor performance. Providing parallelism on several levels (operating system, database system and/or data mining algorithms) can improve discovery performance dramatically.

Due to the polymorphic nature of a business and its data mining tasks to be tackled, hybrid learning should be supported. The spectrum of data mining goals and methodologies provided depends on the diversity of problems which have to be solved.

Finally, when new knowledge has been discovered, some knowledge handling facilities are required to interpret the output. An appropriate tool is a report generator which supports classification trees, rules, associations and so forth. Additionally, a storage mechanism for discovered knowledge makes maintenance far easier.

6.3   BUSINESS PROCESS REENGINEERING TO FACILITATE DATA MINING

If data mining plays a key role in the decision-making process of an enterprise, it might be worthwhile considering restructuring parts of the business organisation. One popular approach for such a rearrangement is business process reengineering (BPR), the philosophy and objectives of which are briefly described in the following subsection. It is then shown how BPR and data mining can be synergised, and what requirements (general, as well as branch-specific) are needed to allow data mining in an enterprise.

6.3.1 Overview of BPR concepts

BPR is a methodology that enables an organisation to make fundamental changes in the way it carries out its business. In BPR, the focus moves from function to process (Fig. 6.1) where, for example, traditional functions such as sales may be overhauled, simplified and reconstituted as processes (Childe *et al.*, 1994).

Figure 6.1
PROCESSES AND PROCESS INITIATIVES IN A FUNCTIONAL ORGANISATION

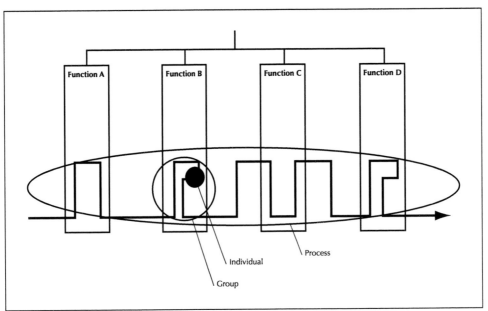

What are the goals of this reengineering effort? Certainly, within an organisation, the main goals can be described as: flexible and simplified processes, empowered employees working in a team environment, removal of non-value-added tasks and, ultimately, more financial controls and lower operating costs to the organisation. But the most successful adopters of BPR see these goals as secondary to the primary goals that fuel an organisation's competitiveness and ability to operate successfully in increasingly difficult market arenas. These goals include: the adherence to quality standards, the managing of suppliers and, most importantly, the responsiveness to customers. The rewards of BPR can be across-the-board improvements in value, quality, customer support and productivity, which are achieved by the new business processes possessing inherent flexibility, agility and responsiveness.

First- and second-order BPR

Supporters of BPR advocate that the reengineering of a company's important business processes should be a revolutionary event (Hammer, 1990), not evolutionary or revelationary. However, recent work on practical application of BPR (Chandler *et al.*, 1996) suggests that an evolutionary approach, more recently called *morphostatic* BPR, may be more acceptable to management and staff than the revolutionary, or *morphogenic*, approach. The morphostatic approach may act to prepare an organisation for the more rigorous application of morphogenic BPR. For this reason, morphostatic BPR is sometimes termed *first-order* BPR, while morphogenic BPR is termed *second-order* BPR. In practice, companies have used first-order BPR to experiment in the use of the method, and are now ready to instigate measures in their organisations to develop BPR as a second-order mechanism.

The role of IT in BPR

BPR is commonly facilitated through the application of appropriate IT. Historically, IT has enabled business processes within functional areas of companies such as manufacturing. However, this application of IT makes the a priori assumptions that companies are optimally organised already, and that the functional approach can manage change elegantly. As a result, adding IT to the existing functionally based processes can guarantee to computerise only non-optimal processes that will be difficult to change. The equation which states that

> *New technology + Existing business practice = New expensive business practice*

is very appropriate in this situation.

In new, lean business processes where non-value added tasks have been removed, IT can enable manufacturing philosophies, e.g. optimised production technology (OPT) or just-in-time (JIT). However, complex problem areas will still exist in reengineered companies. These problems will occur with large and small companies, and basic IT cannot address them. They include the handling of incomplete, conflicting and vague data, the discovery of knowledge in massive data sets, the interpretation of legislation and inter-organisational contracts, the management of change, and the reapplication of an expert's accrued experience and expertise. KBS techniques provide a series of tools that can help to assess, manage and ameliorate these problems (Aikens, 1993). Knowledge engineering, which is the name given to the process of building KBS, applies specialised techniques to acquire, represent and use business process knowledge. There have been a number of reported successes where KBS have added value to business processes, and in fact made their reengineering possible in the first place.

Initiating BPR in an organisation

Davenport and Short (1990) have identified the five major steps to be addressed in first- or second-order BPR (*see* Fig.6.2). These are:

- to develop business vision and process objectives;

- to identify processes to be redesigned;

- to understand and measure existing processes;

- to identify IT levers; and

- to design and build a prototype of the process.

Figure 6.2
FIVE STEPS IN BUSINESS PROCESS REENGINEERING

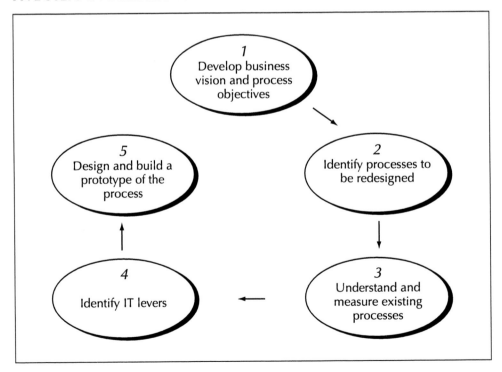

The vision and objectives in the first of these steps is the balancing of factors such as cost and time reduction, the quality of the output of the process, improvements in worklife and the empowerment of employees through process buy-in. In the second step there are alternative strategies that may be used. The most popular of these is to focus on those processes that can have the highest impact on an organisation. Another option is to use techniques that identify those processes that may be most data-rich and can perhaps benefit from the application of IT-enabled BPR. Measurement of the process is the third vital step. If there is no way to gauge how a new reengineered process has impacted on an organisation, either financially or in other more indirect ways, then it may be difficult to champion the changes that BPR may bring. The fourth step can, if directed correctly, lead to massive improvements in how a company carries out its business. IT is central to the success of a great majority of BPR operations, and with technologies such as the Intranet, data warehousing and knowledge-based systems available, quantum leaps can be made in addressing major corporate problem areas. The fifth step is important because it provides the organisation with the visible results of a BPR exercise. It also enables the BPR team to develop a more generic model for further BPR application.

Table 6.1 gives illustrative examples of first- and second-order BPR across the process dimensions of entities, objects and activities. These dimensions enable the appraisal of BPR in any commercial or organisational sector.

The BPR teams

It is crucial that the participants in any BPR activity understand their roles and their interactions with colleagues. The most important participant groupings in a BPR exercise are the steering committee, the design teams and the implementation teams. In addition, key personalities are the project sponsor and champion.

Table 6.1
TYPES OF BUSINESS PROCESSES

Process Dimension and Type	Typical example	First-order BPR	Second-order BPR
Entities:			
Inter-organisational	Order from supplier	Remove non-value-added tasks	Reengineer entire supply chain process
Inter-functional	New product development	Streamline costs	Remove department barriers and form cross-functional product design team
Inter-personal	Approve bank loan	Introduce more systematic, consistent approach	Overhaul thinking behind loan approval process and rethink strategic goals
Objects:			
Physical	Product manufacture	Introduce TQM measures	Introduce fault tracking process: design-to-build
Informational	Proposal development	Focus on key decision makers	New process using decision support systems to ensure consistency, accuracy and quality
Activities:			
Operational	Generate customer quote	Change to business units built around streamlined processes	Introduce external customer leverage. Make quoting process explicit and open to customers
Managerial	Develop budget	Form budget development business unit to bring key people together	Empower business units by making them responsible for costs and profits

Adapted from Davenport and Short (1990).

The steering committee should provide insight and guidance to the overall project, and should comprise staff from the business units or areas affected by the reengineering work. The design teams are comprised of operations managers who will spend at least 50 per cent of their time on the project, while the implementation team members will have responsibility for the detail of the reengineering work and will typically work closely with the design team.

The project sponsor must be capable of envisaging how the reengineering project will address the strategic problems relating to the business, and will be capable of channelling funds and other resources to the various BPR teams. The champion is the BPR expert who works closely with all teams, especially the design team where he or she must co-ordinate the overall design effort. The champion reports frequently to the project sponsor and is fully committed to ensuring the success of the project.

6.3.2 The BPR and data mining synthesis

As has been outlined in the previous subsections, BPR can be formulated as a process of activities operated by involved personnel. The same applies to data mining, which has been outlined in Chapter 4 as a process with appropriate human resources. But, to actually fully profit from data mining techniques and methodologies, an enterprise has to provide information, i.e. data, appropriately.

As described in section 3.4, OLTP was introduced about a decade ago as a method to run transactions upon data within client–server environments. At this stage, many businesses changed their information technology landscape without changing their corporate philosophy. As a consequence, many tasks have been performed outstandingly, whereas decision making became more awkward and cumbersome. This phase correlates chronologically and from a contents point of view with the status quo of business organisations. Functions were modelled as entities within a database, and relations among those entities symbolised their interrelationships. Transaction processing mirrored the information flow between functions.

As a solution to that dilemma, OLAP was introduced, which formed the basis for data warehousing (*see* section 2.3.2). The main functionalities of a data warehouse are the acquisition of internal as well as external data, the building of a central repository containing relevant data and business rules, the analysis of data and the provision of powerful query mechanisms and modern reporting tools. At this stage many enterprises were – and still are – willing to expand their information technology landscape (again), and also to change their corporate philosophy. This phase synchronises well with morphostatic or first-order BPR, as described earlier.

Due to the fact that data mining is a decision support technology, it will be the logical consequence that data mining techniques will be embedded in data warehouses in the very near future. Implanting data mining in data warehouses will influence all existing components: acquisition of data will be supported with machine learning techniques; central repositories will be extended with expert systems functionality; analysis of data will not only be based on traditional statistics, but also on various uncertainty handling paradigms; query languages have to be expanded linguistically; and report tools have to be able to list and visualise not only data but also discovered knowledge. This can be seen as the ultimate goal from the data mining point of view. But, to achieve the required results, business processes have to be reengineered dramatically, a scenario that has been described as morphogenic or second-order BPR. The business process arrangement should be aligned as closely as possible to the data mining process.

Both approaches are goal-oriented. In data mining, the goal is to generate meaningful and useful hitherto unknown knowledge pertaining to one or more databases. The method is to move from OLTP to OLAP incorporated in data warehouses. In BPR, the goal is to create simplified, flexible processes with non-value-added tasks removed. The method is to reengineer existing functional areas or process domains.

Table 6.2 develops the examples given by Davenport and Short (1990) for types of business processes by identifying possible roles for data mining in specific reengineered process areas.

Table 6.2
EXAMPLES OF DATA MINING APPLICATIONS

Process Dimension and Type	Typical Example	Example Data Mining Role
Entities:		
Inter-organisational	Order from supplier	Detect trends and perturbations by cross-linking parts and supplier databases
Inter-functional	New product development	Use data mining to identify customer clusters where minimal product penetration has occurred
Inter-personal	Approve bank loan	Provide closer focus to help identify potential loan customers with lower propensities to lapse on repayments
Objects:		
Physical	Product manufacture	Forecast provision of parts supply for more efficient JIT production
Informational	Bid/proposal development	Cross-link and mine past successful/unsuccessful bids with customer files
Activities:		
Operational	Generate customer quote	Cross-link quote and order databases and mine for generic rules that identify successful transitions from quotes to orders
Managerial	Develop budget	Cross-link business unit costs, profits and budget databases to identify generic rules for profitability

Adapted from Davenport and Short (1990).

The synthesis of data mining and BPR can be viewed at two distinct levels of granularity. This helps to breakdown and simplify the synthesis.

First, there is the coarse-grained synthesis, where the data mining process as a whole has the BPR method applied to it. This view generates a series of requirements which impact upon the technical, human resourcing and management areas in an organisation. In order to apply data mining algorithms to a company database, the technical managers must put in place hardware and data access software that has some OLAP capabilities. If the project is to determine the feasibility of data mining, then a segment or extract of the large OLTP database may be placed on a workstation removed from the day-to-day company operations. The resources in terms of skilled IT staff and marketing staff must be brought together into a multi-disciplinary team, with agreement from their managers that a minimum of 50 per cent of their time is available to address the data mining problem. The management have to ensure that the project has visibility at board level and throughout the organisation, and that sufficient resources are made available to the data mining team.

Second, the BPR method can be applied within the tasks of the data mining process as identified in Chapter 4, although for clarity the distinction between first-order or second-order application of BPR is omitted (see Table 6.3). The goal for these sub-areas – to which BPR can apply – is to produce simple, flexible and manageable processes with clear delineation of who is involved, what the inputs and outputs are and the perceived gains.

6.3.3 Enterprise requirements to allow data mining

In this subsection the requirements of an enterprise to allow data mining is described. A set of general demands that are valid for any company independent of its industrial nature is proposed. Due to the fact that different business branches embody different functionality and processes, two representative branches are used to show the requirements. Building transfer to other key applications, such as administration, science or medicine, is straightforward.

Table 6.3
BPR SYNTHESIS WITHIN DISCRETE DATA MINING TASKS

Data mining process tasks	Area of synthesis with BPR
Human resource identification	Building of inter-disciplinary teams
Problem specification	Develop top-down process goals; prioritise work agenda on processes; identify algorithm/technique applicability to specific processes
Data prospecting	Develop quality measures; ensure data access and availability through data warehousing (or data extracts off-line for pilot/feasibility study)
Methodology identification	Introduce problem–methodology mapping, e.g. using if–then–else scenarios
Data pre-processing	Improve data quality through better input validation; resolve multi-coding and heterogeneity through more homogeneous IT landscape
Pattern discovery	Incorporate the knowledge discovery step as regular task in the business process to ensure knowledge is up to date (a.k.a. knowledge maintenance)
Knowledge post-processing	Develop processes to aid evaluation of knowledge output; identify process to incorporate discovered knowledge into new corporate business models

General requirements

The general BPR requirements can be stated in terms of the success factors for BPR introduction:

- The reengineering effort must be clearly and directly linked to specific business objectives.

- The organisation must establish a strategy for change that anticipates likely obstacles to effective reengineering.

- Support structures must be skilled and empowered to undertake significant change.

- The reengineering effort must be straightforward and practical and feature simple implementation steps.

- Performance is measured and correlated with strategic objectives.

From the viewpoint of data mining, additional enabling technologies have to be provided to set up an appropriate data mining environment:

- incorporation of a data warehouse on top of the IT landscape to profit from the OLAP technology;

- provision of distributed and heterogeneous data access, e.g. using ODBC;

- usage of parallel hardware and data access technologies to gain better performance and allow scalability;

- multi-dimensional servers which can act to pre-cluster data and also improve data access performance;

- modern reporting tools to verbalise, tabulate or visualise knowledge.

The synthesis of the differing BPR and data mining requirements indicates that to be successful, an organisation must take on board a significant resolve for technological change in addition to keeping a clear focus on the business objectives, and must clarify the strategy to achieve those objectives with the key players – employees, customers, and suppliers.

Financial organisations

Financial organisations such as banks, insurance companies, building societies, etc., are at a crucial period in their development. Customers are increasingly, and rightly, more fickle in their selection of financial advisors. They demand a more personalised service, with flexibility in facilities like direct debiting, mortgaging, etc. The financial organisations have invested millions in large OLTP systems that cannot cope with current customer requirements and cannot easily provide customer information for marketing purposes. In addition, fraud detection becomes a highly interesting topic to protect both customers as well the financial institution.

To tackle both problems, additional marketing and security expertise is required. Enquiries about customer services can no longer be based on simple factors like income, job position, etc.; a redirection through a decision-support system without losing any performance makes organisational changes necessary. Access to historical data, such as transaction times series or customer profiles, might be needed to search for necessary information which might not conform to existing authorisation policies.

The requirements in financial organisations focus on a need to address the business demands, aspirations and market expectations of customers and clients while managing the changeover from legacy systems with their attendant massive investment to systems that are capable of OLAP, data warehousing, parallelism, etc.

Manufacturing organisations

Manufacturing covers a broad spectrum of industries, each with its own special production methods. However, carrying out the following may constitute BPR in general manufacturing circles:

- simplification of production flow;

- introduction of JIT;

- flexible production and distribution;

- introduction of concurrent engineering;

- continuous improvement plan;

- establishment of 'quality circles'.

Data mining may most profitably be used in manufacturing to identify areas where improvement exercises should be directed, such as in process control, quality control and maintenance. These three areas are closely interrelated and address traditional business problems directly by providing the tools to achieve efficiency gains, quality gains, better forecasting and planning abilities, and improvements in product consistency.

Data mining processes may also impinge on other processes in manufacturing such as strategic planning, sales or order winning, financial control and supply chain management processes. Manufacturing organisations are continually striving to cut the operating costs of their manufacturing processes. In such an environment the application of data mining techniques is therefore best directed at achieving this goal.

Appendices

APPENDIX 1 CASE STUDIES

A1.1 Cross-selling products

The customer base of a company can be subdivided into a number of customer groups based on the product they have purchased. Cross-sales is the term given to the process of attempting to sell a product to existing customers of the company who are not already customers of that particular product (*see* Fig. A1.1).

Figure A1.1
CROSS-SALES USING DATA MINING

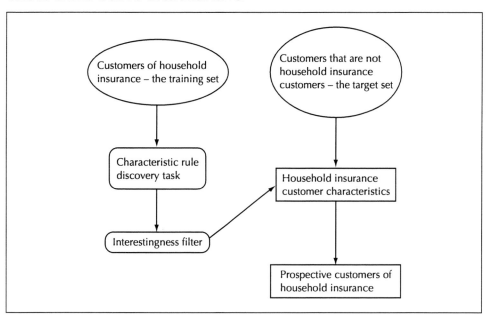

The authors have been working with others in conjunction with a financial institution in Ireland on a project involving such a cross-sales problem (Anand *et al.*, 1997). The client wanted to find characteristic rules defining the type of customers who would buy their various financial products (household insurance, mortgage protection, indemnity bonds and commercial contents insurance) from the data held within their customer database. Clearly, not all the customers of the other products would be suitable for targeting for household insurance and the company can incur large savings only if a subset of the rest of the customer base – those who are more likely to buy household insurance – are targeted for that product.

Within the customer data, the bank has two types of customers: those that already have a household insurance and those who do not. At first glance this seems like a simple classification problem but on closer examination it is obvious that the problem at hand is actually not a classification problem at all. For a classification problem what is required is a third type of customer, one who does not have a household insurance and has refused the offer to purchase one. The first type of customer forms the positive examples, the (missing) third type of customer forms the negative examples and the second type forms the target data set.

For our problem at hand we only have positive examples and a target data set. Thus, rather than using a classification algorithm we need to use an association algorithm to discover characteristic rules. These rules define those characteristics that are prevalent in a particular group of records which in our case is the group of records that pertain to customers who have a household insurance. Given these rules, customers in the target data set with similar characteristics can be targeted with sales campaigns.

The discovered rules are then exploited by targeting customers from the target data set picked using the characteristic rules (see Fig. A1.3 below). At this stage the bank can keep a record of those customers that were targeted but did not buy household insurance and use these records to refine the characteristic rules making them more accurate, or they can use these records as negative examples and then use a classification algorithm to discover classification rules.

An additional source of data was externally procured survey data. This survey data was spatially joined with the customer database of the bank (Fig. A1.2) – the resulting larger data set being a much enriched version of the bank's customer database.

Figure A1.2
A GEOGRAPHICAL MAP OF THE CUSTOMER DATABASE

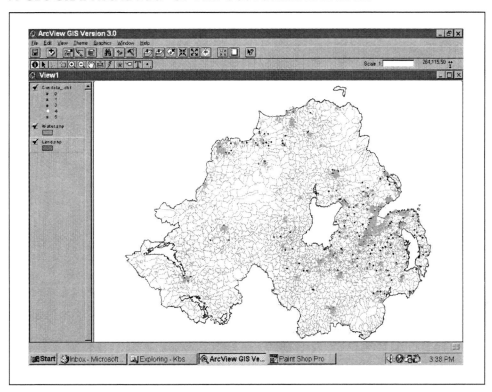

To tackle the outlined problem, a generalised association algorithm, EAR, was used that forms part of the Mining Kernel System. The EAR algorithm allows the incorporation of support and uncertainty thresholds as well as (simple and inter-attribute dependency) syntactic constraints. For each product or service provided by the financial institution, the positive subset of records from the enriched customer database was extracted, i.e. those records where the corresponding customer had bought the product. Each of these subsets was then mined separately to discover characteristic rules for the corresponding product. Depending on the support threshold, the number of discovered rules changed dramatically. To distil useful information from the knowledge mass, interest-based filtering techniques were applied.

An interest measure was defined based on the deviation of the characteristic rules discovered for the product from the *norm*. The norm in our case is the support for these characteristics within the complete customer base of the company, i.e. a characteristic rule is interesting if it is a characteristic of the customer of a product rather than the customer base in general.

Examples of discovered rules are

> *if HouseholdInsurance = Y*
> *then Occupation = Skilled and Status = HonCommits and*
> *NetCreditTurnover > 4000 and AccountType1 = Current*
> *with support = 12.56% and interest 0.74*

> *if Household Insurance = Y*
> *then CusNodeps = 0Dep and CusYrnetavgbal = Zero_1500 and*
> *Children= 4*
> *with support = 10.93% and interest = -0.77*

The first of these rules may be interpreted in a straightforward manner, i.e. 'customers in skilled professions with a status of *HonCommits* and *NetCreditTurnover* greater than £4000 in a current account are more likely to buy household insurance'. The large negative interest measure for the second rule suggests a different interpretation: 'customers with no dependants, with a small yearly net average balance, living in an area where there is a high percentage of children per household are less likely to buy household insurance'. There could potentially be a number of reasons for this, however – what data mining has done is to highlight this anomaly that needs further investigation. The sorts of questions that the domain experts must ask themselves now are: 'Is there a domain-specific reason for this?' or 'Are we pitching this product in a way that makes it unattractive to customers with these characteristics?' etc.

Figure A1.3 presents some of the rules graphically. Here, the oval nodes represent attributes used to specialise the rule specified by the path from the root node to the node preceding the oval node, while the rectangular nodes represent the specialisation attribute value. The numbers shown in the rectangular nodes are the support and interest of the rule. The light grey nodes represent rules that have an interest value less than or equal to another rule that the present rule is a specialisation of, while the darker grey nodes represent rules where the specialisation attribute has improved the interest value of the rule. Non-shaded nodes represent rules where the specialisation has decreased the interest in the rule.

Figure A1.3
VISUALISATION OF CHARACTERISTIC RULES

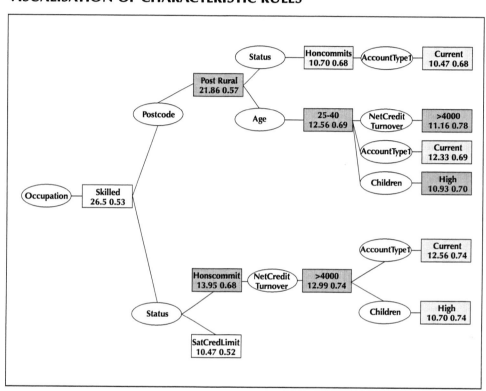

A1.2 Fraud detection

Mapfre, Spain's largest insurance company, has been data mining with ANGOSS KnowledgeSEEKER (*see* Appendix 2.2) to curb the rising problem of fraud within its motor claims division.

Until quite recently, Mapfre's fraud investigation team had been working on gut feel and intuition. They had developed a simple system of rules, based on their experience, that they applied to randomly selected claims and investigated those which they felt were suspicious in any way.

Two problems were faced by Mapfre. First, they were not detecting enough fraud with the current system of rules. Second, the problem with fraud detection in general is that fraud is an ever moving target and the patterns and rules change frequently. Under their current system of detection, Mapfre's ability to spot those changes and thus react to them was limited. Mapfre believed that data mining would be the solution to their problem and so analysed claims data collected over the previous four years with ANGOSS KnowledgeSEEKER to identify all areas of potential claims fraud.

Detailed models were then produced in KnowledgeSEEKER highlighting even niche patterns of fraud. The *FraudDetected* field was selected as the dependent variable and the decision tree was built. KnowledgeSEEKER segmented the data exposing where fraud was higher or lower than the 10 per cent level shown overall. For example, the level of fraud fluctuated dramatically between the different types of insurance policy offered by Mapfre from as low as 2.8 per cent in Cars – Comprehensive up to 24.9 per cent in all motorcycle policies (*see* Figs A1.4 and A1.5).

Figure A1.4
KnowledgeSEEKER'S DECISION TREE SHOWING THAT THE LEVEL OF FRAUD IN MOTORCYCLE CLAIMS IS FOUR TIMES THE AVERAGE OVERALL

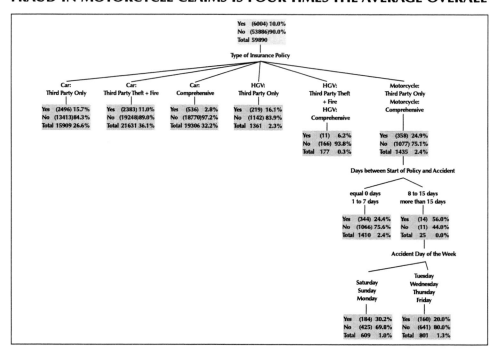

Figure A1.5
USING THE COLOUR-CODED TREE MAP FEATURE IN KnowledgeSEEKER
MAKES THE PATTERNS OF FRAUD EVEN EASIER TO SPOT, THE DARK
COLOUR REPRESENTING THE LEVEL OF FRAUD IN EACH OF THE NODES
OF THE TREE

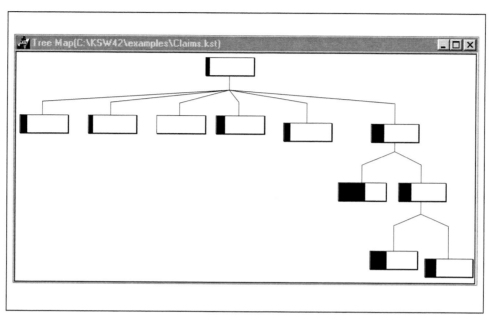

KnowledgeSEEKER then generated a comprehensive set of rules that
were built into an expert system by Complex Systems SL (Fig. A1.6).
The expert system now monitors every claim entered by every clerk at
Mapfre and cross checks them against KnowledgeSEEKER's rules. The
system has been set to flag all claims with a probability of fraud
greater than 60 per cent. This equates to 4 per cent of all claims being
investigated. The fraud investigation team are now investigating fewer
claims and have a significantly better hit rate. To detect changes in the
patterns of fraud, Mapfre randomly analyses one in fifty claims and
uses KnowledgeSEEKER's *compare* function to measure the results
against KnowledgeSEEKER's models. Any differences are then
highlighted, and new rules are generated and built into the expert
system. This way, changes are detected at the earliest opportunity and
can be reacted to immediately.

With such an improvement in efficiency, Mapfre naturally expected
significant savings to be made and budgeted that these would be in
the region of 500 million pesetas (£2.5 million). The actual savings

made went way beyond all expectations and exceeded 2 billion pesetas (£10 million) within the first 12 months of implementation.

Figure A1.6
KnowledgeSEEKER AUTOMATICALLY CONVERTS THE DECISION TREE INTO A SET OF BUSINESS RULES THAT CAN BE IMPLEMENTED IN AN EXPERT SYSTEM

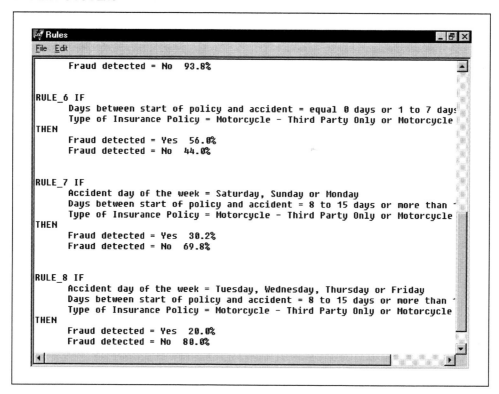

A1.3 Retail

Retail 'basket analysis' has been a much publicised application of data mining. Many other retail applications, however, can have much greater strategic value. One key decision area for most retailers, for example, is store siting – opening stores in unsuitable locations wastes investment opportunities and creates an ongoing drain on a company's profits.

Halfords, part of the Boots Group, is the UK's leading retailer of motor accessories and related leisure items such as mountain bikes. Halfords was originally a high-street operation. In recent years, though, high-street stores have suffered from increasing costs and parking restrictions. As with many retailers, in keeping with changing national shopping patterns, Halfords began several years ago to reshape its business around edge-of-town superstores.

In an ambitious store expansion programme Halfords needed to find profitable locations to site new stores. As the move to edge of town was a recent change, the company had little acquired experience on which to base site selection. They knew that many factors played a part in making a store successful, but not how they combined to give rise to a particular store's performance. The factors included:

• site factors such as access from town and from main roads, local competition and co-located stores which, while not directly competitive, attract the right 'shape' of customer for Halfords;

• population factors describing the demographics of the site's catchment area;

• store factors reflecting management policies such as stock composition.

Management needs quantified knowledge of these factors and their effects, and the ability to predict revenue with sufficient confidence that this can be applied to hypothetical new stores.

Halfords used the Clementine data mining tool (see Appendix 2.2) to analyse historic sales and site profile data from their existing stores. Working from 150 randomly selected stores, the project combined 1993/94 sales figures with data from a site quality questionnaire, store specific information and census data describing the demographics of each store's catchment area. A model was developed to predict store revenue; this was tested on existing stores.

A year before this, Halfords had commissioned a statistical regression model to address the revenue prediction problem. This model was never deployed, as its accuracy was unsatisfactory and it provided little information on how combinations of factors produced revenue levels.

The model built using Clementine gives much greater accuracy than
the regression model; a comparison is shown graphically in Fig. A1.7.
Very importantly, it also has significantly more explanatory power.
Halfords combined Clementine's neural network and rule induction
facilities, and the induced rules helped senior management to
understand the reasons for differences in store performance.

Figure A1.7
SALES: PREDICTED AGAINST ACTUAL

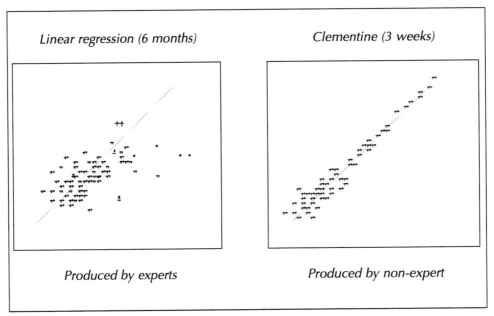

Two further aspects of this application are worthy of note:

- While the regression model was created by professional statisticians,
  Halfords themselves brought Clementine in-house and assigned a
  business expert (a senior financial manager in the property division)
  to the task of model building.

- Timescales for the actual data mining activity were very short.
  Halfords spent six months assessing alternative approaches to
  tackling the problem. A further three months was spent collecting
  and generating the data required. Once the data had been gathered
  and the user trained, the first models were built in less than a week.
  These initial prototype models were not sufficiently accurate for
  deployment, but the final, highly accurate versions were delivered in
  only a few weeks.

The system has been used since 1995 to drive investment decisions about the choice of new sites for Halfords superstores. As the models are built directly from historical store data, they can be continuously refined and improved as more stores are opened and more sales figures recorded.

The following are some of the streams and models created during the project by Halfords themselves:

• Figure A1.8 shows for each case, the integration of data on the store, its site and the demographics of the catchment area.

Figure A1.8
STAGE 1 – COMBINING DATA SOURCES

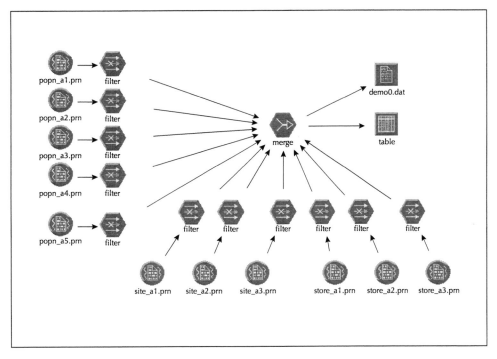

• Figure A1.9 shows the addition of new measures and descriptive variables based on expert knowledge.

• Figure A1.10 shows partitioning the data into training and test sets, building models using a neural network and rule induction, and evaluating their performance.

Figure A1.9
STAGE 2 – ENRICHING THE DATA

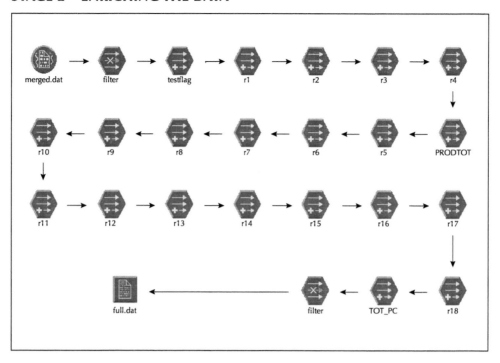

Figure A1.10
STAGE 3 – BUILDING AND EVALUATING MODELS

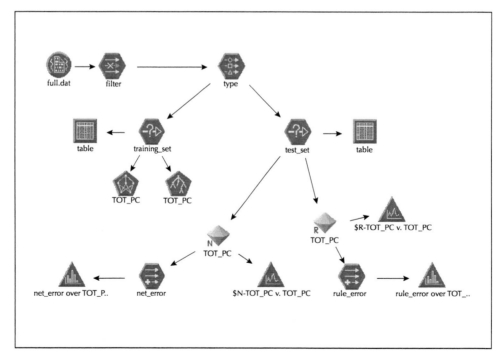

A1.4. Mining the World-Wide Web

The World-Wide Web (WWW) is one of the fastest growing information sources to date. However, due to its highly volatile nature and strong diversity, tracking down required information can become a tedious task. Various powerful search engines, softbots, crawlers, WWW agents, etc. have been developed to search through unstructured data, some of which use modified data mining techniques (Etzioni, 1996).

Another aspect of Web mining is the discovery of knowledge from data generated by Internet servers, i.e. the analysis of behavioural patterns of users interacting with commercial sites. The Data Mining Group at BT Laboratories applied knowledge discovery techniques to analyse their own electronic commerce web-site I-Mart (Mace, 1996).

The individual preferences of each user can be dynamically monitored. For example, advertisers may soon be able to target consumers by employing an automated process which infers marketing intelligence from WWW-based data. As a result the success of advertising campaigns could be directly assessed, empowering the marketer with information which would allow them to justify the cost of their advertising.

Navigation visualisation

To discover typical user navigation paths and analyse them qualitatively, it is necessary to consider the order in which a user has browsed through I-Mart. Netmap is an interactive visualisation tool designed for the analysis of relationships inherent in large volumes of data (*see* also Appendix 2.2). The graphical displays produced by Netmap are designed to highlight formal and informal networks, and its functionality allows for analysis of these networks. Through structured queries it is possible to obtain an understanding of various processes which exist hidden within the data.

The idea of Netmap is based on the concept of *nodes* and *links*. For example, one could define a set of nodes to be a set of unique telephone numbers, and links between these nodes to be communication between the telephones (i.e. A calls B would connect node A to node B). A link between two nodes is simply represented as a direct straight line connecting one to the other, and it is the patterns that these links show which are of key interest.

In analysing the data collected from I-Mart, the data mining tool Netmap gave a detailed picture of agglomerate navigational patterns by showing the connectivity between page pairs. In this application, nodes were defined to be the different page numbers that were accessed and a link was defined as the navigation from one page to another. Focusing on displayed pages (static and dynamic) and system pages (templates and services) with more than ten requests and drawing the node width proportional to the number of connected pages the display given in Fig. A1.11 is obtained. Here, it is possible to identify the pages of the system which carry the majority of traffic (seen as wide nodes) and the pages to which they are connected. This helps the service provider to visualise the structure of the I-Mart site and understand the usage of the system services and templates.

Figure A1.11
NAVIGATION LINKS

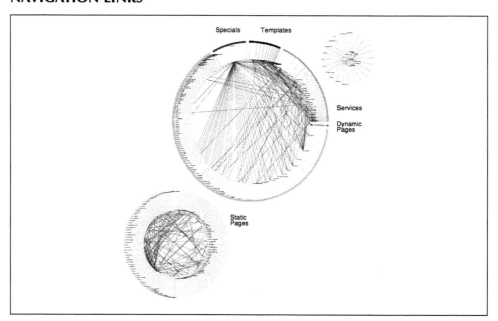

In addition to this type of visual investigation based upon user-defined groups (e.g. page functions), Netmap supports another powerful grouping strategy known as *emergent* grouping. This ignores the node ordering specified by the user and clusters nodes based solely on the links present on the current display. Each emergent group is based upon how the nodes share their linkage. Those nodes which share more linkage with each other than they do with any other nodes are defined to be an emergent group.

Making use of this clustering algorithm BT analysed the groups of pages that have naturally emerged as a consequent of accumulative user behaviour within the site. It was found that all the groups consisting of entirely static page members are a product range along with the front page for that product. Figure A1.12 gives an expanded view of one of the larger groups and finds these to be a range of mobile phones. A total of nine different static groups emerged. These product types can be considered as the most popular, and those products which do not feature here might need to be given a higher profile in the catalogue (e.g. advertise a product on the login page) in order to obtain a better response.

Figure A1.12
EMERGENT GROUP 'MOBILE PHONES'

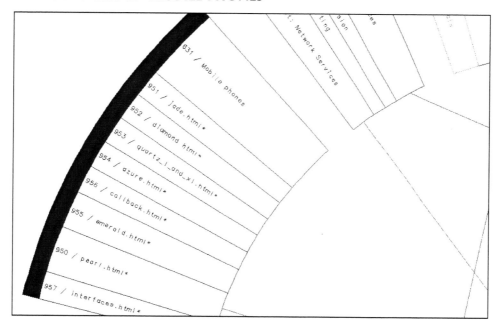

By observing the link patterns it is also possible to infer knowledge about product-to-product interest. For example, a link from the *telephones* front page to *telephones and answering machines* front page implies that users might have an interest in both types of products. Likewise, links between *cordless phones* and *network services* implies that if users are interested in one product then they are likely to be interested in the other.

Page association

Supplementary to the qualitative analysis using Netmap, quantitative measures for page associations can also be obtained by employing association rules (*see* section 5.1.1). Given an ideal data set, we would be searching for the following types of rule:

- Find all rules that have *commit the shopping basket* as the consequent, i.e. is there a set of pages which leads to a sale, and what is the support and confidence of each rule/sale?

- Find all rules that have page X as the antecedent. This could be helpful if we want to know the effect of removing page X from the catalogue. That is, what other pages will be affected?

- Find all rules relating product X with product Y. These rules may help Web-site structure design. If product X and product Y are significantly related then a direct hyperlink should be made from one product to the other.

- Find all rules with a confidence greater than P per cent. This can be used to enhance proxy caching (pre-fetching Web pages) or knowledge of what to advertise.

An example of the rules found are listed in Table A1.1, which shows inter-product confidence where the quantitative likelihood of a user looking at product type Y given that they have looked at product type

X is observed.* Notice that the confidence for the majority of the rules is less than 21 per cent, implying that users are, in general, only interested in one type of product.

Table A1.1
PRODUCT TO PRODUCT INTEREST

Antecedent	Consequent	Support %	Confidence %
Cordless phones	Phones	2.15	20.71
Phones	Mobile phones	2.15	15.53
Phones	Phone systems	1.58	11.36
Phones	Special phones	1.94	14.20
Phone systems	Phones	1.58	34.09
Special phones	Phones	1.94	43.02
Mobile phones	Answering machines	1.05	7.52
Telephone & AM	Answering machines	2.73	42.62

It may be assumed that users who are interested in *Telephone & Answering machines* will also show a high degree of interest in the *Answering machines* (or vice versa) since they are both very similar product types. We see that the confidence of this rule is relatively high. The other two exceptions can be explained by customer confusion. The confidence levels of *(Phone systems)* ⟶ *(Phones)* and *(Special phones)* ⟶ *(Phones)* are both quite high, but the reverse of these rules appears to be the opposite. This is because the majority of users are interested in normal phones but access *Special phones* and *Phone systems* mistaking these to be a range of household telephones. After realising their mistake, they go back one page and then access *Phones.*

---

*   The rule *A* ⟶ *B* (*P*%) denotes that if a user visits page *A* during a session then he or she is likely to visit page *B* in the same session (or may have already visited *B*) with probability *P* per cent, and not a user navigation from page *A* to page *B* with probability *P* per cent.

More association rules have been found within the data, e.g. *attractive items of a product range*, or *antecedent of an electronic transaction*. The technique can be further extended to include particular services, templates, errors, etc. of the catalogue to obtain a deeper understanding. For example, it might be possible to find that the system has an inherent error at one particular point seen by the following rule, enabling the identification of the location and eventually the cause of this error:

(Page A, Page B, Page C) $\longrightarrow$ *Error X*

The search for association rules has been proved to be a very effective mining technique for learning about the usage of the I-Mart system. It emphasises how important it is for the service provider to develop a fluent structure which encourages users to visit certain pages.

APPENDIX 2 A BRIEF MARKET OVERVIEW

A2.1 Checklist

We provide a checklist for evaluating data mining products which considers the polymorphic nature of real-world projects. The list is based on Steps 4 to 8 of the data mining process described in Chapter 4 (the first three steps, 'data prospecting', 'human resource identification' and 'problem specification', are not usually software-supported). In addition to the given software features, usual criteria, such as hardware requirements, operating system support, user support, price and so forth, have to be considered when acquiring information about a data mining system.

Domain knowledge elicitation	Applicable	Yes/No
Hierarchical generalisation trees	☐	☐
Attribute relationship rules	☐	☐
Attribute dependencies	☐	☐
Others	☐	☐

Methodology Identification	Applicable	Yes/No
Traditional statistics		
Standard functionality*	☐	☐
Exploratory data analysis	☐	☐
Log-linear modelling	☐	☐
Linear regression	☐	☐
Multivariate analysis	☐	☐
Others	☐	☐

---

*   With standard functionality we mean basic functions provided by statistics such as average, minimum, maximum, mean, median, standard deviation, correlation, etc.

Machine learning techniques		
Rule induction	☐	☐
Nearest neighbour	☐	☐
Kohonen networks	☐	☐
Multi-layered perceptrons	☐	☐
Others	☐	☐
Uncertainty-based techniques		
Bayesian belief networks	☐	☐
Fuzzy logic	☐	☐
Rough sets	☐	☐
Evidence theory	☐	☐
Others	☐	☐
Database techniques		
Set-oriented approaches	☐	☐
Attribute-oriented induction	☐	☐
Statistical databases	☐	☐
Others	☐	☐

Data pre-processing	Applicable	Yes/No
Data types		
Ordinal	☐	☐
Numerical	☐	☐
Nominal	☐	☐
Dates	☐	☐
Others	☐	☐
Data Formats		
Relational databases		
(Oracle, Sybase, DB2, ...)	☐	☐
ODBC	☐	☐
ASCII files	☐	☐
Statistical packages (SPSS, SAS, ...)	☐	☐
Multiple databases	☐	☐
Others	☐	☐

Scrubbing facilities

	Applicable	Yes/No
Data cleansing techniques	☐	☐
Missing values	☐	☐
Noise handling	☐	☐
Data selection	☐	☐
Others	☐	☐
Others	☐	☐

Pattern discovery	Applicable	Yes/No
Discovery tasks		
Associations	☐	☐
Classification rules	☐	☐
Sequential patterns	☐	☐
Characteristics	☐	☐
Clustering	☐	☐
Deviation detection	☐	☐
Regression	☐	☐
Temporal modelling	☐	☐
Others	☐	☐
Parallelism	☐	☐
Data warehouse support (OLAP)	☐	☐
Others	☐	☐

Knowledge post-processing	Applicable	Yes/No
Knowledge presentation		
Visualisation	☐	☐
Natural language	☐	☐
Tables	☐	☐
Knowledge export (formats)	☐	☐
Knowledge filtering		
Thresholds (confidence, support, ...)	☐	☐
Statistical independence and deviation	☐	☐
Syntactic constraints	☐	☐
Knowledge validation	☐	☐
Others	☐	☐

A2.2 Market overview

We now give a brief overview of a representative set of data mining products available on the market and map their technical capabilities onto the checklist given in the previous section. Due to the diverse nature of projects, no judgements on the tools are being made, some of which might tackle some problems perfectly and others not at all. Note that there are literally dozens of data mining products and tools available nowadays, the exhaustive evaluation of which would be beyond the scope of this book. The information given here is also available on-line from the authors' data mining site (http://iserve1.infj.ulst.ac.uk:8080) and is updated on a regular basis.

A quite comprehensive survey including commercial products as well as research prototypes has been done by McClean and Scotney (1996). Other surveys have been carried, most of which can be found on the Internet (*see* Appendix 6).

No entry for a criterion denotes that the information was not available, whereas '–' denotes that the functionality is not supported by the product.

Product/supplier:	Alice / ISoft
Domain knowledge elicitation	attribute generalisation
Methodology identification	
Traditional statistics	–
Machine learning techniques	rule induction
Uncertainty-based techniques	–
Database techniques	–
Data pre-processing	
Data types	numeric, alphanumeric, flags
Data Formats	Access, dBase, Foxpro, Paradox, ODBC, Excel, Lotus, SAS, SPSS
Scrubbing facilities	data cleansing
Pattern discovery	classification
Knowledge post-processing	
Knowledge presentation	charts, rules, trees, reports, SQL queries
Knowledge filtering	min number and min % of records, x^2 test
Knowledge Validation	–

Product/supplier:	Clementine 4.0 / Integral Solutions Ltd
Domain knowledge elicitation	definition of relevant properties
Methodology identification	
Traditional statistics	standard functionality, linear regression
Machine learning techniques	rule induction, neural networks, Kohonen nets
Uncertainty-based techniques	–
Database techniques	
Data pre-processing	
Data types	numeric, symbolic, flag, date, time
Data formats	Informix, Ingres, Oracle, Sybase, ASCII, ODBC, SPSS, SAS, Excel
Scrubbing facilities	data cleansing, missing values, noise, data selection
Pattern discovery	classification, sequential patterns, clustering, regression, temporal modelling, associations
Knowledge post-processing	
Knowledge presentation	graphs, charts, rules
Knowledge filtering	thresholds depending on the algorithm
Knowledge validation	–

Product/supplier:	Data Engine 2.0 / MIT
Domain knowledge elicitation	fuzzy rules
Methodology identification	
Traditional statistics	standard functionality, deviation detection
Machine learning techniques	rule induction, neural networks, Kohonen nets
Uncertainty-based techniques	fuzzy logic, neuro-fuzzy techniques
Database techniques	–
Data pre-processing	
Data types	numeric, alphanumeric, date, time
Data formats	ODBC, ASCII, Excel
Scrubbing facilities	data cleansing, missing values, noise, data selection
Pattern discovery	classification, clustering, regression, signal processing,
Knowledge post-processing	
Knowledge presentation	graphs, charts
Knowledge filtering	thresholds depending on the algorithm
Knowledge validation	–

149

Product/supplier:	Intelligent Miner / IBM
Domain knowledge elicitation	attribute generalisation
Methodology identification	
Traditional statistics	standard functionality
Machine learning techniques	rule induction, neural networks
Uncertainty-based techniques	–
Database techniques	
Data pre-processing	
Data types	numeric, alphanumeric, date, time
Data formats	DB2, ASCII, import from Oracle, Sybase
Scrubbing facilities	data cleansing,
Pattern discovery	association, classification, sequence patterns, characteristics, clustering, deviation detection, temporal modelling
Knowledge post-processing	
Knowledge presentation	charts, reports, various export options
Knowledge filtering	
Knowledge validation	–

Product/supplier:	KnowledgeSEEKER IV 4.2.1 / Angoss Knowledge Engineering Ltd
Domain knowledge elicitation	
Methodology identification	
Traditional statistics	standard functionality
Machine learning techniques	rule induction
Uncertainty-based techniques	fuzzy logic, Bayesian belief nets, evidence theory
Database techniques	
Data pre-processing	
Data types	categorical, continuous
Data formats	dBase, Paradox, SQL*Net, ODBC, ASCII, SAS, SPSS, Excel, Lotus, etc.
Scrubbing facilities	missing values, noise, data selection, NULL categories, break apart, heterogeneity resolution
Pattern discovery	association, classification, sequence patterns, clustering, deviation detection, parallelism, data warehousing
Knowledge post-processing	
Knowledge presentation	charts, rules, (cross-)tables, SQL, Prolog
Knowledge filtering	thresholds depending on the algorithm
Knowledge validation	–

Product/supplier:	Mineset 1.1 / Silicon Graphics Inc.
Domain knowledge elicitation	
Methodology identification	
Traditional statistics	standard functionality
Machine learning techniques	rule induction, CBR, neural networks
Uncertainty-based techniques	Bayesian belief nets, rough sets
Database techniques	
Data pre-processing	
Data types	Informix, Oracle, Sybase, ASCII
Data formats	nominal, ordinal, discrete, continuous
Scrubbing facilities	missing values, noise
Pattern discovery	classification, clustering
Knowledge post-processing	
Knowledge presentation	charts, decision trees
Knowledge filtering	thresholds depending on the algorithm
Knowledge validation	–

Product/supplier:	Netmap 4.13 / ALTA Analytics Ltd
Domain knowledge elicitation	
Methodology identification	
Traditional statistics	standard functionality, deviation detection
Machine learning techniques	
Uncertainty-based techniques	
Database techniques	
Data pre-processing	
Data types	strings, numeric
Data formats	DB2, Informix, Ingres, Oracle, Red Brick, Sybase, ASCII, SPS, SPSS
Scrubbing facilities	data cleansing, missing values, noise, data selection, heterogeneity resolution
Pattern discovery	association, classification, sequence patterns, clustering, deviation detection, temporal modelling, data warehousing
Knowledge post-processing	
Knowledge presentation	net maps based on nodes, satellites and links
Knowledge filtering	
Knowledge validation	–

Product/supplier:	XpertRule Profiler 3.0 / Attar Software Ltd
Domain knowledge elicitation	production rules
Methodology identification	
Traditional statistics	standard functionality
Machine learning techniques	rule induction, genetic algorithms, neural networks
Uncertainty-based techniques	–
Database techniques	
Data pre-processing	
Data types	numeric, alphanumeric, date
Data formats	ASCII, ODBC, SAS, SPSS
Scrubbing facilities	data cleansing, missing values, noise, data selection
Pattern discovery	association, classification, sequential patterns, clustering, temporal modelling
Knowledge post-processing	
Knowledge presentation	charts, trees, rules
Knowledge filtering	
Knowledge validation	–

APPENDIX 3 GLOSSARY

The following list contains terms and their explanations which are used throughout this book regularly. The number on the right of each term denotes the section in which the term is dealt with in more detail, if applicable. A comprehensive data mining and knowledge discovery terminology can be found in Kloesgen and Zytgow, (1996).

Association rule   **5.1.1**

Association rules represent sets of attribute-value pairs in a data source that tend to occur together in the data, limited by support and confidence thresholds.

Bayesian belief networks   **5.2.3**

Bayesian belief networks represent a graphical technique that is used to model uncertain information within an environment based on relationships between variables of the environment. These networks are underpinned by well established Bayesian probability techniques allowing for information to be inferred.

Business process reengineering (BPR)   **6.3**

BPR is a methodology that enables an organisation to make fundamental changes in the way it carries out its business. In BPR, the focus moves from function to process where, for example, traditional functions such as sales may be overhauled, simplified and reconstituted as processes.

Case-based reasoning (CBR)   **5.2.2**

CBR is a technique which is used to solve problems by finding similar, previous cases (stored in the case base), retrieving its appropriate case-specific information and employing a similar solution.

Characteristic rule   5.1.4

Characteristic rules define those characteristics that are prevalent in a particular group of records. They represent the sufficient condition for membership of the group.

Classification   5.1.2

Classification is the discovery of rules that discriminate between two or more classes based on their attributes.

Client–server   2.3.1

To minimise network traffic and simplify data consistency, the database itself is stored on the server and numerous clients are loosely connected to it. 'Loosely' means that only queries are sent to the server side and the requested data is then sent to the requesting client.

Clustering   5.1.5

Clustering is concerned with grouping data into similar categories, which are unknown in advance.

Confidence   4.8.1

The belief that if the antecedent of a rule is true then the consequent is also true.

Data mining

The 'non-trivial process of identifying valid, novel, potentially useful and ultimately understandable patterns in data' (Fayyad *et al.*, 1996).

Data mining methodologies   5.2

Data mining methodologies can be subdivided into the five categories traditional statistics, machine learning techniques, uncertainty-based techniques, database techniques and visualisation. The choice of the appropriate methodology depends on the type of data mining task at hand (*see* also section 4.5).

Data mining process   **4**

The process of the steps human resource identification, problem
specification, data prospecting, domain knowledge elicitation,
methodology identification, data pre-processing, pattern discovery and
knowledge post-processing. The last two steps are likely to move
through various refinement stages.

Data pre-processing   **4.6**

Data pre-processing consists of filling in missing values, identifying
and removing outliers, resolving heterogeneity and coding the data as
well as reducing its dimensionality and size.

Data prospecting   **4.3**

Data prospecting analyses the stage of the data with respect to
relevant attributes, accessibility and data attribute population as well
as distribution and heterogeneity.

Data scrubbing

See Data pre-processing

Data segmentation

See Clustering

Data warehousing   **2.3.2**

Data warehousing principally integrates legacy systems, i.e.
operational data, within a corporation to provide an enterprise-wide
view to decision making.

Decision support   **1.1**

IT support for managerial decision making in information intensive,
ill-defined fields.

Deviation detection   **5.1.6**

A data mining task aimed at discovering and explaining deviations
from norms.

Domain knowledge   **4.4**

Information specific to the application domain not belonging to data which is usually provided by a domain expert or an expert system.

Fuzzy set theory   **5.2.3**

Representation of uncertain data in crisp or fuzzy sets based on membership degrees and functions, which allows approximate reasoning.

Genetic algorithms   **5.2.2**

Efficient search algorithms that model evolution. Through effective exploration and exploitation they tend to navigate local mining, arriving at globally optimal solutions.

Human resources   **4.1**

Human resources involved in data mining are the domain expert (knowledge about the application area, e.g. a medical doctor), the data expert (knowledge about the structure of the data, e.g. a database administrator) and the data mining expert (knowledge about data mining techniques, e.g. a knowledge engineer).

Interestingness   **4.8.1**

Interestingness is accepted as a subjective measure as what is interesting to one person may not be interesting to another. The measure takes into consideration novelty of the knowledge, conspicuousness and deviation from the expected.

Knowledge discovery

Up-to-date term for data mining in related literature. In industry (as well as in this book), however, the term data mining is still used to describe the whole process of knowledge discovery, instead of the single step of pattern discovery.

Knowledge post-processing   **4.8**

Knowledge post-processing consists of filtering out uninteresting and obvious patterns, as well as validating interesting patterns.

Machine learning   3.3

Machine learning is the area of artificial intelligence which tries to automate learning. Learning by example, learning by observation and connectionist learning are some of the techniques used to emulate human learning. Machine learning algorithms form the basis for most data mining tools.

Multi-dimensional database (MDD)   2.3.3

A database which is designed for on-line analytical processing (OLAP) and structured as a multi-dimensional hypercube with one axis per dimension.

Neural networks   5.2.2

Non-linear predictive models that learn through training and resemble biological neural networks (brains) in structure.

On-line analytical processing (OLAP)   3.4

The two most often used definitions are 'the dynamic synthesis, analysis and consolidation of large volumes of multi-dimensional data' (Codd *et al.*, 1993) and 'fast analysis of shared multi-dimensional information' (Pendse and Creeth, 1995).

Pattern discovery   4.7

Pattern discovery is the stage of the data mining process in which appropriate algorithms are employed to automatically find new patterns from pre-processed data.

Regression   5.1.7

A statistical technique used to find the best-fitting relationship between a target (dependent) variable and its predictors (independent variables).

Rough set theory   5.2.3

A theory to reason from imprecise data by investigating structural relationships. The technique provides insights into data, allowing the elimination of redundant and irrelevant attributes.

Rule induction   5.2.2

Rule induction involves the creation of a model of the environment using sets of data describing the environment. This model is generated by generalising specific data to a more abstract level using inductive biases and inference rules.

Sequential patterns   5.1.3

Sequential pattern discovery is similar to discovery of associations. The difference is that sequential pattern discovery techniques discover association across time.

Support   4.8.1

The support for a discovered rule is the number of records in a data source that satisfy the rule.

Temporal modelling   5.1.8

Temporal modelling is concerned about rules which describe the general changing behaviour of a set of data over time, e.g. the influencing factors for stock price fluctuations.

APPENDIX 4 REFERENCES

Aikens, J. (1993) 'Business process reengineering: where do knowledge based systems fit?, *IEEE Expert*, 8(1), 2.

Anand, S. S., Hughes, J. G., Bell, D. A. and Patrick, A. R. (1997) *Tackling the Cross-Sales Problem Using Data Mining*. Proceedings of the First Pacific-Asia Conference on Knowledge Discovery and Data Mining, Singapore.

Anthony, R. N. (1965) *Planning and Control Systems: A Framework for Analysis*, Harvard Business School, Division of Research, Boston, Mass.

Bigus, J. P. (1996) *Data Mining with Neural Networks*, McGraw-Hill.

Butler Group (1996) *Data Warehousing Technology Stream Journal*, June. http://www.butlergroup.co.uk.

Buytendijk, F. A. (1995) *OLAP: Playing for Keeps* (maintenance and control aspects of OLAP applications). http://www.xs4all.nl/~fab/olapkeep.html.

Byte Magazine (1995) 'Data Mining', October.

Chandler, J. W., Palvia, P. C., Thomson, J. D. and Zeltmann, S. M. (1996) 'Process engineering at FedEx', *Communications of the ACM*, 30(2), 99–107.

Childe, S. J., Maull, R. S. and Bennett, J. (1994) 'Frameworks for understanding business process reengineering', *International Journal of Operations and Production Management*, 14(12), 22–34.

Codd, E. F., Codd, S. B. and Salley, C. T. (1993) *Providing OLAP to User-Analysts: An IT Mandate*. White Paper produced by Codd & Date, Inc.

Conspectus (1996) 'Data warehousing and decision support environment', February.

Davenport, T. H. and Short, J. E. (1990) 'The new industrial engineering: information technology and business process redesign', *Sloan Management Review*, 11.

Etzioni, O. (1996) 'The World-Wide Web: quagmire or gold mine?', *Communications of the ACM*, 39(11), 65–8.

Fayyad, U. M., Piatetsky-Shapiro, G., Smyth, P. and Uthurusamy, P. (eds) (1996) *Advances in Knowledge Discovery and Data Mining*, AAAI/MIT Press.

Frawley, W. J., Piatetsky-Shapiro, G. and Matheus, C. J. (1991) 'Knowledge discovery in databases: an overview', in G. Piatetsky-Shapiro and W. J. Frawley (eds), *Knowledge Discovery in Databases*, AAAI/MIT Press, 1–27.

Gorry, G. A. and Scott Morton, M. S. (1971) 'A framework for management information systems', *Sloan Management Review*, 13(1), 55–71.

Hammer, M. (1990) 'Reengineering work: don't automate, obliterate', *Harvard Business Review*, 90, 104–12.

Heckerman, D., Mamdani, A. and Wellman, M. P. (guest editors) (1995) 'Special issue on real-world applications of Bayesian networks', *Communications of the ACM*, 38(3), March.

Inmon, W. H. (1992) *Data Warehouse*, Wellesley.

Kenan Sahin (1996) *Multidimensional Database Technology and Data Warehousing*, http://www.kenan.com/acumate/byln_mdw.htm.

Kloesgen, W. and Zytkow, J. M. (1996) 'Knowledge discovery in databases terminology', in U. M. Fayyad et al. (eds), *Advances in Knowledge Discovery and Data Mining*, AAAI/MIT Press, 573–92.

Langley, P. and Simon, H. A. (1995) 'Applications of machine learning and rule induction', *Communcations of the ATM*, 38(11), November.

Mace, J. (1996) 'Internet usage analysis: a detailed study of an electronic commerce web-site', in *Proceedings of the Workshop on Data Mining in Real-World Databases at the International Conference on Practical Aspects of Knowledge Management,* Vol. 1, Basel, Switzerland, October.

McClean, S. and Scotney, B. (1996) *The Data Mining Report,* Unicom Seminars Ltd.

Pendse, N. and Creeth, R. (1995) 'The OLAP report', *Business Intelligence,* August.

Piatetsky-Shapiro, G. (1991) 'Discovery, analysis and presentation of strong rules', in *Knowledge Discovery in Databases,* AAAI/MIT Press, 229–48.

Red Brick Systems (1995) A Red Brick White Paper, http://www.redbrick.com/rbs/whitepapers/datawh_wp.html.

Scott Morton, M. S. (1960) *Management Decision Systems: Computer Support for Decision Making,* Harvard University Press, Boston, Mass.

Sigmore, R., Craemer, J. and Stegman, M. O. (1995) *The ODBC Solution: Open Database Connectivity in Distributed Environments,* McGraw-Hill.

Small, R. D., Edelstein, H. A. (1997) 'Scalable Data Mining', http://www.twocrows.com/whitep.htm

Srinivas, M., and Patniak, L. M. (1994) 'Genetic algorithms: a survey', *IEEE Computer,* 27(6), June.

APPENDIX 5 FURTHER READING

Below is a list of standard references in the field of data mining and related subjects, which is by no means exhaustive. Other, more technical, references can be found in the proceedings of the international conference on Knowledge Discovery and Data Mining.

A5.1 Books

Data Mining Techniques for Marketing, Sales, and Customer Support
M. J. A. Berry and G. Linoff, John Wiley & Sons, 1997.

A very good book based in the business sector, which describes different data mining techniques exhaustively and gives practical examples for clarification. It also covers related subjects, such as OLAP and data warehousing.

Data Mining
P. Adriaans and D. Zantinge, Addison-Wesley, 1996.

This book offers a comprehensive introduction to data mining, aiming to provide essential insights and guidelines to help making the right decisions when setting up a data mining environment.

Data Mining with Neural Networks
J. P. Bigus, McGraw-Hill, 1996.

This book gives a good introduction to data mining and neural networks and shows the applicability of the technology for knowledge discovery. It is sometimes a little bit biased towards the neural network philosophy, without showing its pitfalls.

Knowledge Discovery in Databases
G. Piatetsky-Shapiro and W. J. Frawley (eds), AAAI/MIT Press, 1991.

The first collection of technical articles in the field of data mining and knowledge discovery.

Advances in Knowledge Discovery and Data Mining
U. M. Fayyad, G. Piatetsky-Shapiro, P. Smyth and R. Uthurusamy (eds), AAAI/MIT Press, 1996.

A second comprehensive collection of technical articles about research into and application of data mining and knowledge discovery.

A5.2 Journals

International Journal on Knowledge Discovery and Data Mining
Kluwer Academic Publishers

A quarterly published journal which covers all areas of research and applications in data mining and knowledge discovery.

IEEE Expert and Intelligent Applications
Volume 11, Number 5, October 1996.

A special issue on data mining, which contains numerous articles about the principles and technologies of data mining and knowledge discovery.

Communications of the ACM
Volume 39, Number 11, November 1996.

This special issue on data mining provides a representative selection of articles including the topics data mining process, data warehousing, statistics, mining business databases, the World-Wide Web and scientific data.

IEEE Transactions Knowledge and Data Engineering
Volume 8, Number 6, December 1996.

This issue includes a special section on the mining of databases which contains about a dozen technical articles about research at the authors' research laboratories.

A5.3 Technical and Management Reports

IBM Data Mining Technology
Claudia Gardner, 1996.

A technical report from IBM which covers the data mining process, data mining operations, data mining techniques and data mining applications.

The Data Mining Report
Sally McClean and Bryan Scotney, Unicom Seminars Ltd, 1996.

A management report which covers the principles of data mining, related technologies, key applications and tool functionality. It also provides various case studies and a very comprehensive taxonomy of existing products and tools on the data mining market.

APPENDIX 6 INTERNET RESOURCES

There are various data mining related locations on the Internet of which we mention below a few useful starting points:

- **Knowledge Discovery Mine**

  http://www.kdnuggets.com

  Probably the most comprehensive data mining site, with a wide range of up-to-date information, many links to other sites and the electronic newsletter *KDD Nuggets*.

- **The Corporate KDD bookmark**

  http://www.cs.su.oz.au/~thierry/ckdd.html

  Contains many research papers and industry pointers related to data mining, data warehousing, decision support and databases, mainly focusing on commercial applications.

- **IBM's data mining site**

  http://direct.boulder.ibm.com/bi/tech/mining/index.html

  An overview of IBM's data mining business intelligence philosophy, which also covers related disciplines such as data warehousing, OLAP, databases, etc. Links to related work at the research laboratory and available data mining products.

- **Microsoft's Decision Theory and Adaptive Systems Group**

  http://www.research.microsoft.com/research/dtg

  An overview of data mining related research at Microsoft.

- **The University of Ulster Data Mine**

  http://iserve1.infj.ulst.ac.uk:8080

  The authors' data mining page.

- **Data Warehousing on the Internet**

  http://www.datawarehousing.com

  Dedicated to documenting all data warehousing related information on the Internet.

- **Datamine-L**

  datamine-l-request@nautilus-sys.com

  Datamine-L is an unmoderated mailing list which has been set up to provide a world-wide e-mail forum for discussing practical applications of data mining, data warehousing and knowledge discovery. To subscribe to the list, send an e-mail to the above address with the text 'subscribe datamine-l' in the body of the message (leave the subject field empty).